PREWD and PREJUDICE

This book is dedicated to the county of Norfolk
and its magnificent motto – 'Do Different'.

Oh Martha, this Trunch is a terrible sight;
There's nothing much happens by day or by night.
They don't have the things we depend on in Town,
And there's gangs of them digging for spuds in the ground.
It looked awfully easy, despite all the mud,
So I just gave a hand at this digging for spuds;
Now my aching back makes me wish I could stand
Where the Charing Cross Road runs down to the Strand.
(*The Muntons Of Moorgate*)

PREWD and PREJUDICE

a Norfolk Exile

Chris Sugden and Sid Kipper

Prewd and Prejudice

First published in 1994 by
Mousehold Press
Constitution Opening
Norwich, NR3 4BD
Reprinted 1994
Reprinted 1995
Reprinted 1998

Cover design and illustrations by
Patrick Loan and Terence Loan.

ISBN 1 874739 03 X

Printed by Watkiss Studios
Biggleswade
Bedfordshire

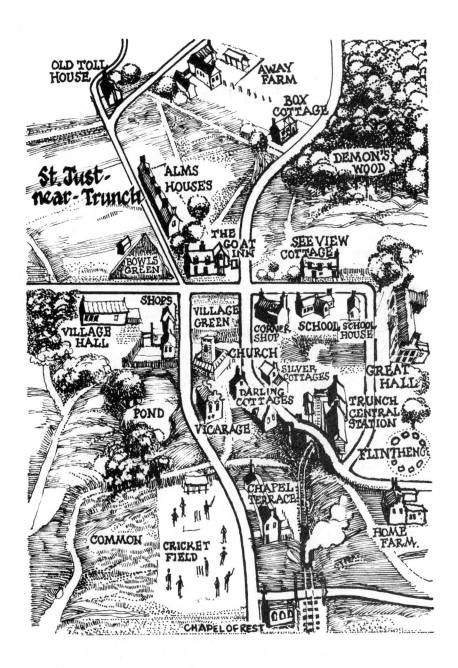

Acknowledgement:

Many thanks to Dick Nudds, who made various contributions
to this book in its early stages and who is still well remembered
in St Just-near-Trunch. Thanks also to Dick for his permission to
use some of the songs included.

I am also indebted to a number of other people – if you are
one of them, please consider yourself hereby thanked.

MARCH 1904

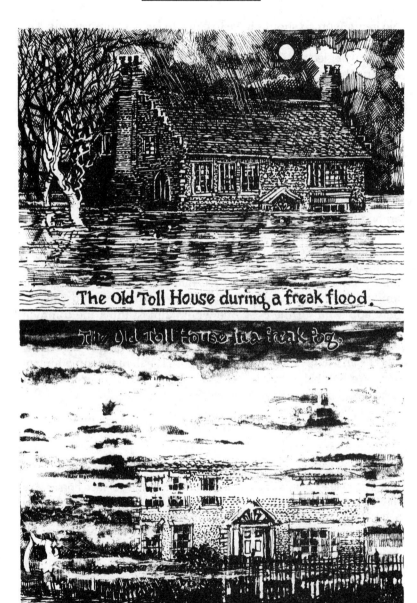

The Old Toll House during a freak flood.

The Old Toll House in a freak fog.

1

25 March, Friday

No gentlewoman should have to come to such a house as this. The landlord should be horsewhipped for the shameful way in which it has been neglected. Or rather, since the landlord is a member of the nobility, his agent should be horsewhipped. Indeed, I would carry out the punishment myself, were it not for a suspicion that he would enjoy it.

The village of St Just-near-Trunch itself is no better. Plants grow everywhere and the natives do nothing to discourage them. These wretches live dismal lives, devoid of most of the necessities of life. There is no milliner for miles, a manicure is quite unobtainable, and Harrods flatly refuse to deliver. I am only 150 miles from London but I feel as far from civilisation as any missionary cast among the savages of the South Seas.

However, since I am compelled to come here and write this diary I must make the best of it. To this end I have already managed to engage the services of a housemaid. She is Maud Kipper, whose family have vegetated in these parts for more generations than their limited numeracy would allow them to calculate. Maud was the only applicant for the post: one would almost think the common people of the area are unaware of the pleasures of serving their betters. How I will manage to train a simple country girl to be of the slightest use I do not know, but I suppose I shall make something of her. We will begin by scrubbing the house from cellar to attic. If necessary I shall supervise the work myself.

****

Dorian Prewd Esq. died in April 1903 in suspicious circumstances — including at least one member of the court and a string of race horses. His wife, Miriam, brazened this out, declaring that all men had their little peculiarities and it would be a fine world indeed if those who had bought privilege were not allowed to enjoy it. Then she discovered he had left her penniless, facing a life of poverty and hardship.

Appalled at this prospect she went to the only person she could really trust, a publisher by the name of Penguin. She knew she had some talent as a writer, but what should she write? What would sell? Penguin told her that the book world was in a slump and nothing was selling. There was, however, one slim hope. Penguin felt that in years to come there might be

2

a market for the diaries of Edwardian women living in the country. What about those living in town, she enquired hopefully. No, they definitely had to live in the country, he thought, and was prepared to back his opinion by paying Miriam to go and live in the country for a year, to write a diary for publication at some future date.

What could she do? She loathed the country. More than that she loathed the idea of her fashionable friends discovering that she was actually *living* there. Yet there was no alternative. So she stiffened her upper lip and agreed to go, on condition that she went somewhere so remote that no word of her presence there would ever reach Town. Thus the village of St Just-near-Trunch in Norfolk was selected for her exile. As she herself wrote: 'Even if anyone does come to hear of it, they will never believe that such a place really exists.'

26 March, Saturday

Scrubbing away the dirt has only revealed further decay. Everything in this house is painted brown – which is, of course, as it should be – but it is such an unfashionable brown. Maud says it is called 'muckwash'. When I asked her what sort of a colour that might be she replied that it mightn't be a colour at all, but a material. This left me none the wiser.

✳✳✳✳✳✳✳✳✳

The house Mrs Prewd rented stood slightly outside the village of Trunch, in the neighbouring parish of St Just-near-Trunch. It was built in 1771 as a toll house on the Suffield to Mundesley turnpike, but the road never reached it. The project was abandoned when the backers realised that no one actually wanted to travel from Suffield to Mundesley, let alone pay for the privilege. By 1904 the thing remaining was the large toll house jutting out into the bleak Norfolk countryside, at the corner of Side Street and Back Lane. It was useless to its owner, Lord Silver-Darling, who was no doubt delighted to get it off his hands for a while.

The house no longer stands, nor does any complete picture of it survive. It was completely destroyed in a raid by German naval airships on the night of 19/20 January 1915.* Rumours still persist that the raid was the result of a personal favour owed by the Kaiser to His Lordship, who was then able to collect on the insurance.

* See Arthur Banks, *A Military Atlas of the First World War*, Pernell, 1975.

3

29 March, Tuesday

Today I called on the vicar of St Just-near-Trunch, the Rev. Ashley Mullett. This was the first social call I have made since coming to this wretched backwater and it was hardly a success. I had expected him to be eager to welcome to his flock someone with a modicum of refinement and education. When I sent in my card, however, his man returned with a message: 'His Reverence is busy attending to a fallen woman, and could you return in an hour or so?'

I walked on into the heart of the village which seems to consist chiefly of a few shops, a low den called The Goat and the church itself.

Norfolk, I have been told, is a county rich in beautiful churches, and just such a gem is wasted here on those without the refinement to appreciate it. I spent an hour looking round the building. I was accompanied by a pathetic, cringing wretch, who I took at first to be a homeless beggar, but later found to be the curate. The church is especially noted, I gather, for its magnificent Saxon doorknob. Apparently it once had a marvellous collection of gold and silver plate too, but in recent years this has gone missing in mysterious circumstances.

On returning to the vicarage I was informed that Rev. Mullett's visitor was still with him, having fallen further than His Reverence had at first thought, and therefore needing considerably more of his time. So I was forced to exchange intelligent conversation for Maud's inanity.

Much of what Maud says is incomprehensible. She is such a strange girl. She tells the most alarming tales of her relatives and I wonder whether I have been wise to engage her somewhat limited services. Beggars, as my Uncle Wesley used to say, cannot be choosers. But I have always before been a chooser.

****

Mrs Prewd may have had her doubts about engaging Maud Kipper, but my researches into the diary have been greatly assisted by Maud's great-nephew, Sid Kipper, who is a mine of information on local history and customs, as well as providing many of the old songs which I have used to illustrate the text:

Aunt Maud died in 1933, from consumption. She consumed two bottles of whisky for a bet. Tragic, it was. Well, I mean, she won the bet but she couldn't collect her winnings. However, my uncle George got the money for her, and he spent it the way he reckoned she would have wished. He bought a load of beer for himself.

Sid is also something of an expert on the history of St Just's church, having written an essay about it at primary school:

The old church was built by the Sextons, who come over here from the continent. I don't know which continent – America I suppose. Anyhow, they built the church and they ran it for years, until it was taken over by the Anglicans, who'd come over in the same boat. You know, the Anglicans and the Sextons. The Anglicans run the church to this very day, but we've only got one Sexton left. At one time I believe they did have a load of posh crockery what the Lord used to eat his supper off, but that all went missing about the time my Great Uncle Albert ran off to sea. Of course, they used to have a load of lead on the roof, but that vanished too. About the time my uncle George went on his world cruise that would be. They don't seem to have a lot of luck with metal up at the church. I've often thought about travelling myself, but I don't suppose you'd get far on an old doorknob.

I have visited the church many times, mostly to claim sanctuary when the villagers have grown angry at all my questions. It has an atmosphere of peace and tranquillity which is quite different to that other social centre of the village, the Old Goat Inn. Sitting in the church, or indeed standing in it – or even lying down – you feel the presence of Truncheons past, passing back in an unbroken chain to times long before Mrs Prewd's visit. Somehow you feel that the things which seemed so important before, such as this book for instance, are of no consequence whatsoever. Many people have told me the same thing.

30 March, Wednesday

What a delight for me when the vicar returned my call of yesterday, and had the kindness to take tea and muffins, and cake, and indeed anything else he was offered. He may be only a vicar, but he has the appetite of an Archbishop.

Rev. Mullett is a man of middle years with the remains of nice

5

manners. Educated in London, he was the incumbent of one of those dreaming spires of Oxford until he felt a calling to leave there and come to work as a sort of missionary amongst the unlettered degenerates of this area. Or, as he calls them, 'the common folk'. In particular his mission is to fallen women and he assures me that he spends much of his time touring the area in search of them.

It must be said that Rev. Mullett shows signs of having 'gone native', as my Uncle Wesley would have said, or, as we say in London, 'back to basics'. It is, perhaps, inevitable that ten years in a place like this would leave its mark. I am only thankful that my own stay is to last but a single year, or, as it is now, 360 days, 15 hours and some minutes. However, I do feel that one must entertain doubts about a man of decent education who sits in one's parlour, chewing on a straw and spiting fragments out on to the rug. I have decided that I must excuse him his idiosyncrasies and make a firm acquaintance of him, since we are clearly two of the few civilised people hereabouts.

I pointed out to Rev. Mullett that I found the lack of refinement of the area depressing, but he defended his common folk stoutly. 'Mrs Prewd,' he said, 'it is not right to be too harsh on them. They have their own ways, which are somewhat rough and ready, and often hard for us to understand, but underneath it all they have livers of gold.' I am still at a loss for the meaning of this strange statement.

As the vicar was leaving I apologised for having missed church on Sunday, but assured him that I would not fail to attend on Friday if he would let me know the hour of the service. He looked at me quizzically. 'Friday?' he said. 'Well, it is Good Friday,' I answered. 'Oh yes, I had thought of having some sort of a gathering, but changed my mind when I saw upon what date it fell. It does not do to tempt fate, Mrs Prewd.' With this astonishing pronouncement still hanging in the air he mounted his donkey and left.

****

The Reverend Ashley Mullett was known during his life for his good works. 'Fallen women', as they were then known, were a speciality of his. Fallen men, on the other hand, were of no interest to him. They were forced to seek the help of the rector of a nearby parish, whose talents lay more in that direction.

6

The Rev. Mullett was laid to rest in the churchyard of St Just-near-Trunch – on more than one occasion, as it happens – but eventually passed away in 1936. He was much loved in the village because of the way he fitted in with local habits – precisely what Mrs Prewd complained about.

'Back to basics', incidently, seems to have had a very precise meaning in 1904, unlike today, when it has become quite meaningless.

APRIL 1904

Palm Sunday, Easter Monday –

Thus we start our roundelay;

Shrove Tuesday, Ash Wednesday –

Keep you on, we're past half way;

Maunday Thursday, Good Friday –

That's Easter week, alack-a-day.

(Anon.)

1 April, Good Friday

How very strange it seemed not to be in church on Good Friday morning. After all, this is a day of penance and fasting, and there seems little point in going to that sort of trouble in private, where others cannot gain from the example. Since it is a public holiday I allowed Maud light duties such as chopping wood, cleaning the chimneys, and so on. I do not think I shall be so generous in the future, however, as she was quite ungrateful.

Maud did throw some light on Rev. Mullett's remarks about the day. It seems that Good Friday this year coincides with a local festival known as 'All Idiots Day'. As one might expect with people of this sort it is the latter which takes precedence.

At about two o'clock I glanced out of the window to see a peculiar sight. Up the lane came a procession of ruffians, some playing drums and other such unmusical instruments. As they passed the hedge I saw that they wore a strange assortment of head-dresses, constructed from the crudest of materials. I eventually realised that these pitiful creations were supposed to resemble the heads of various animals, though I challenge anyone to discern the species.

As the column passed I noticed that the rear was brought up by something quite different. It was immediately recognisable to anyone who has visited the zoological gardens in Regent's Park as the head of a polar bear.

I was pondering the significance of all this when Maud rushed in crying 'Look, Mrs Prewd, there come the idiots!' Before I could correct her grammar she had taken off to follow them.

Later, as I tried to drink an appalling cup of tea, which I had been forced to make myself, I heard a knock at the door. I answered it, but there was no one there. This happened three more times. On the last occasion I heard a mocking voice from beyond the hedge call out 'You're an idiot!' At once I caught up my umbrella and set off to investigate the source of this challenge. There, in the lane, was a man draped in what seemed to be a rug made from a polar bear – in the manner of Uncle Wesley's tiger-skin, of which he was so proud. Clearly here was the ringleader of the trouble makers, wearing what was almost certainly stolen from his betters. In the interests of justice

I proceeded to give him a sound thrashing, which I hope he learned from, as it cost me a perfectly serviceable umbrella. That which had many a good downpour left in it was all used up on one shower.

****

The All Idiots Day festivities of the Trunch area have, over the years, been a wonderful mixture of tradition and improvisation. Some elements have clearly survived through the mists of time. The procession of animal heads, for example, may well have its origins in the rituals of the Iceni, who lived in the area before the Romans. It has been suggested that Iceni meant 'people of the horse',* and throughout the region many horsy people may still be found. These people probably invented the tradition of parading a man dressed as a horse. Over the years cocky people must have added the cock, sheepish people the sheep, and so on.

Having processed through the village the revellers would split up to carry out all manner of jests, japes and jokes. Some of these practical jokes were themselves traditional, such as knocking on a door and running away, while others were pure inspiration.

Sid: My Great Uncle Albert used to specialise in impractical jokes. He used to do things like balance a bucket of water on a sliding door or make an apple pie bed with a real pie. But I've done one or two good ones in my time. Once I put a pig in the gents toilet of the Old Goat Inn and no one noticed for three days. Another time I gave my mother Dot a cup of tea in bed – that took her by surprise.

It was 68 years since All Idiots Day and Good Friday last coincided, but everyone remembers that, as a consequence, the dowager Lady Silver-Darling never left the Hall again, and the church had to be reconsecrated. It is no wonder the vicar saw fit to avoid any repetition of such goings on.

* Lethbridge, T.C.(1964)*Witches: Investigating an Ancient Religion* , p.79.

2 April, Saturday

This evening Maud returned with the most shocking news. It seems that Lord Silver-Darling's son, Doyley, was brutally assaulted this afternoon in the lane outside the house. He had been taking part in the day's festivities when he was attacked by a mad woman who launched a crazed assault upon him, inflicting severe injuries before he could escape. How strange that I heard nothing.

3 April, Sunday

What am I to do? I am in despair. If, as I now learn, Doyley Silver-Darling was the man in the polar bear rug, then I must be the mad woman.

****

The polar bear skin in question was a treasured possession of the Silver-Darling family. It's origins are obscure – so much so that the locals have been forced to invent theories of their own as to how it came to be in a little Norfolk village.

Sid: They reckon it all happened when Gerald Silver-Darling went on what they call the Grand Tour. The Tour become a lot less Grand when his ship dragged its anchor while putting in to Cromer and ended up off the West coast of Greenland. In fact they would have discovered the North-West Passage a century early if they hadn't been desperately trying to sail south-east.

Anyhow, on a hunting trip ashore Gerald got himself eaten by this polar bear. The crew didn't know what to do, so they caught the bear and brought it home. Well, the rich was always quick to discard the weak and embrace the strong, so the Silver-Darlings married it off to their youngest daughter.

The marriage went very well by all accounts, but that become illegal by accident when they brought in the law against bear baiting in 1835. This broke the bear's heart, and he pined to death, so they had him made into a hearth rug.

4 April, Monday

I have reached a decision. While I maintain that anyone who goes around behaving like a member of the working classes must expect to get the occasional thrashing, if he is the son of a Peer of the Realm he is bound to have delicate sensibilities. I have therefore decided to visit Doyley Silver-Darling and explain the facts frankly to him. To this end I have sent to the Hall for an appointment, which has been granted for tomorrow.

The event has caused a great stir in the village. It seems they think it perfectly normal for a future member of the House of Lords to parade the lanes dressed in a bear skin and are well aware of the identity of its occupant. They therefore assume this assault to have been committed by a person of unsound mind – perhaps a socialist – who they now fear may be still at loose. The only thing which prevents a general panic is their belief that the culprit is suffering from a monomania directed against bear skins. Nearby North Walsham has therefore cancelled a visit of the Brigade of Guards.

****

Doyley Silver-Darling (full name Doyley Quinton Ferdinando Silver-Darling) was a man who enjoyed life to the full. His family had lived in St Just-near-Trunch for generations and took a keen interest in local affairs. Indeed, they were personally involved in many of them.

In 1904 Doyley was living in London, but he visited the village frequently to keep abreast of family business. While in Town he was often to be seen at the theatre or music hall, and he was especially fond of the operas of Gilbert and Sullivan. This was hardly surprising, as he was conceived at a performance of HMS Pinafore in 1878 and born – in the same box – at the premier of The Pirates Of Penzance in 1879. Lord Silver-Darling, by the way, did not mind these interruptions to his entertainment. He only attended the operas in the mistaken belief that the words were written by Fred Gilbert, who wrote his Lordship's favourite song, 'The Man who Broke the Bank at Monte Carlo'. We now know, of course, that Arthur Sullivan's collaborator on these works was W. S. Gilbert, of whom his Lordship had never heard.

5 April, Tuesday

What a charming man Doyley Silver-Darling is. One can instantly spot his breeding, even through the bandages. His somewhat surly butler, Herring, showed me in, and he made every effort to rise to greet me. When he had sunk back into his bath chair he gave me half a smile, that being all he was capable of, and asked 'Now what can I do for you, Mrs Prewd?' I was at a loss for words. How could I tell this man, clearly so handsome and athletic beneath the plaster, that it was I, a woman, who had caused his injuries? What might that do to such a fine and noble thoroughbred? I could not be the one to add insult to grievous bodily injury.

12

So I told him that I had felt I should visit him, since the awful incident had occurred outside my house. I sympathised with his injuries and agreed that these were, indeed, terrible times that such a thing could happen. I left as quickly as was seemly.

At least I shall not have to face him again soon as he is leaving for London to convalesce the moment he is fit to travel.

****

We know a good deal about Doyley Silver-Darling because his butler, Herring, later wrote two volumes of autobiography called *I Did It* and *What I Saw.*

I recall an incident which occurred on one of our many trips to the family estates in St Just-near-Trunch. It would have been in the Spring of 1903 or 1904 when my master called me one morning to dress Him. 'Your morning suit, Sir?' I enquired, to which he replied, 'No, you idiot, I will wear the bear skin.' By this I knew He was going slumming in the village.

Later, as I was replating the silver in my pantry, I was summoned to go to Him quickly in his rooms. I found Him in a sorry state. 'If you think I look bad you should see the other fellow,' He groaned, as I helped Him to bed.

The affair was a cause célèbre in the village and had a strange sequel when a Lady from London came to see Him. I thought that if she had come all this way to His sick bed there might be something between them which I could turn to my advantage. My hopes were dashed, however, when it transpired that she was, in fact, living locally.

My master was horrified by her. He quickly decided that if He was to be subjected to appearances by this woman while He remained in St Just, then we must return to London at once.
(*I Did It* , Chapter 3 – My Way)

6 April, Wednesday

With all the excitement of recent days I have neglected my task of recording the day-to-day life of the area, although it is beyond my comprehension why anyone should be interested in such a dreary subject.

Sunday, of course, was Easter Day, and breakfast was late. Maud seemed surprised when I berated her, saying that we must wait for the eggs to arrive 'of course'. Eventually there was a knock at the back door, and four and a half minutes later my breakfast eggs were served. I told Maud that if there was a problem in getting eggs on time then someone should get the chickens up earlier of a morning, rather than let them perch about until all hours of the day. She began some excuse involving her brothers, but I made it clear that I do not accept excuses – only results. She sulked all day, but I ignored that, being too concerned over the business of the polar bear.

Sunday led to Monday and Tuesday was dominated by my visit to the Hall. Now, perhaps, I can concentrate on getting this house and garden as I wish them to be, training Maud to the apron, and trying to establish contact with a few decent people, if such there be in these uncivilised parts.

****

Mrs Prewd's breakfast eggs were late for good reason – they came all the way from nearby Knapton.

Sid: It weren't that we didn't have enough 'hen fruit' in Trunch. It was because in Knapton they had the old Easter custom of egg rolling. They used to roll painted eggs down the hill from Knapton towards Trunch every Easter morning. I don't know what they done it for – that seem daft to me. We never done it. We used to have our own custom. We used to wait at the bottom of the hill and carry the eggs off for breakfast.

Eggs had great symbolic meaning for rural people. They were used in witchcraft and divination, as well as in traditional medicines. They were reckoned to have an opposing effect to rhubarb, and many perfectly healthy people regularly wore an egg and rhubarb poultice just to be safe.

All of this shows the difference between Mrs Prewd's limited urban horizons and the more profound understanding of rural life. What she was waiting for were not merely eggs, but symbols. And, as any countryman will tell you, you can't rush a symbol.

11 April, Monday

Reverend Mullett called today to ask for help in making new kneelers for the church. I quickly agreed that Maud would be delighted to help him, in her free time. As a more personal contribution I offered my advice. I suggested green for the north-west nave and yellow for the south-west. These were the colours of my late husband's regiment and whenever I see them I think of him proudly marching at the head of the column, his hand on the lead of the official mascot.

I asked the vicar how his work among fallen women was progressing, but the question seemed only to depress him. 'These are terrible times, Mrs Prewd,' he replied. 'I have been unable to find a woman in need of my services for some days now.'

This lack has left him unsatisfied and I fully sympathise with his feelings. It is so frustrating when one wishes to patronise the working classes and they are not available.

****

St Just's Church is what the ordnance survey describes as a 'Church without a tower'. That is to say, the tower is completely surrounded by the church. This gives a double nave, the other two sides being cloisters.

The church was designed this way after a furious row between Hugo de Gimingham, then Lord of the Manor, and the Bishop of Norwich. Sir Hugo wanted to build a church pointing north to south, but the Bishop ruled that it must point east to west, as usual. This would have meant the church pointing straight at the great hall: 'Like unto sum grate diggette,' as Sir Hugo put it. As he was a very violent and sexually active man, I can understand him not wanting to be constantly reminded of the swift arrow of God's judgement.

After much coming and going of letters, emissaries and 'gifts', the Bishop agreed to the compromise we see today. This placed the altar in the correct place, while sparing Sir Hugo's conscience – such as it was. In his letter of permission the Bishop wrote: 'In this way shalle it be behelde by all that this hollie building pointeth in no direction but upwarde, to the grater glorie of He who ruleth over all.' Sir Hugo, thinking this was a reference to himself, agreed.

14 April, Thursday

This afternoon I made the acquaintance of the village schoolmistress. It happened during a walk round the area which I took in search of some redeeming feature – a mission which was as great a failure as I had feared it would be.

As I approached the Board School I heard a dreadful noise. Then I saw a writhing heap of children in the road. As they were in my path I set about them with a stout stick, which I carry for just such eventualities. I was surprised to find, as the curs fled my blows, that at the bottom of this heap was a young woman. I had begun to reprimand her for setting such a bad example when she interrupted me to say that she had been attempting to stop the fight. I, of course, reprimanded her further for interrupting me, and then asked who was supposed to be in charge of the urchins. She instantly broke down in tears and admitted they were her responsibility. 'Thank goodness the boys have gone over to Southrepps,' she wailed. I did my best to comfort her by telling her to snap out of it and behave like an Englishwoman. This seemed to help and she stopped beating her head against the wall.

Miss Pickerel – for that is her name – is a mere slip of a girl and has only recently become a certificated teacher. She has, like myself, come to this dreadful place from a more civilised background – though not, of course, as civilised as my own. The poor thing is appalled at the brutality of life of the common people and most especially of their common children. She feels it is her job to turn these swine into pearls. I had to disabuse her of this notion. The most she can hope for is to domesticate them a little. I offered to pass on to her a few tips of my Uncle Wesley's, if she cared to take tea with me tomorrow. She was pathetically grateful, and insisted on kissing my hem. This was not an altogether unpleasant experience.

****

The Trunch Bored School was founded by Lord Silver-Darling in 1872. It was obviously much needed – not least by the stonemason who carved the name over the door. Its stated purpose was 'to ensure that all the children of the village receive an education fitting to their station, and to instil proper respect for Church, State and the property of others'. The Silver-Darlings, of course, went to Eton.

16

In its early years the Bored School had a patchy history. His Lordship saw it mainly as a source of cheap labour, and he would often cart off the whole school, teacher included, to work on the estate or in the house. This was eventually stopped by the Attendance Officer, though His Lordship was furious. He wrote to the Chief Education Officer, Dr C. Gamble:

> What better training for working life can there be than the experi-
> ence of work itself? Indeed, I venture to say that in years to come
> such 'work experience', as I call it, will become an accepted way
> of keeping these young ruffians out of trouble. The devil finds work
> for idle hands, so it is our duty, surely, to keep those hands busy.

No doubt, as His Lordship turns in his grave over the many changes since his time, he at least wears a self-satisfied smile about this particular matter.

15 April, Friday

This village schoolmistress is indeed an unfortunate creature. She is a victim of her parents' wish to better her. Determined to pull them-selves up from the slime of the lower orders they decided from the start that their daughter should become a teacher. Realising that their own names, Ethel and Stanley, marked them immediately for what they were, they christened her 'Miss', and made sure that she was diligent in her lessons. Her education having been completed with a course at the Norwich Training College, she obtained the post of schoolmistress in St Just-near-Trunch.

Being of poor stock she has no natural authority, and finds it impossible to maintain order. She has prepared excellent lessons on such topics as 'The Tributaries of the Amazon', 'The Life Cycle of the Tsetse Fly', and so on, but her ungrateful charges show not the slightest interest or respect.

As I allowed her to pour my tea I gave her some advice on discipline, gleaned from the wisdom of my late and much lamented Uncle Wesley. 'Never work with children – they are animals' seemed hardly tactful, so I tried some of his other aphorisms. 'The little chil-dren suffer if they come unto me' seemed more appropriate, al-though neither of us could glean much from 'The man is father to the child.'

17

What delighted Miss Pickerel most were some of the practical suggestions I was able to make. She brightened up a good deal, promising to try them out at once. She now realises that what these people need is discipline rather than knowledge. As I pointed out to her, what use have they for knowledge? They are better off remaining ignorant. Even a little knowledge can be a dangerous thing and it is our responsibility to protect them from such dangers.

She went home much pleased, and I dare say that if she applies my advice wisely she will remain in her post for many years to come.

****

Miss Pickerel did stay at the village school for a long time. She was still there when Sid's father, Henry, and uncle George attended some twenty years later. Even when Sid himself went to the school it had changed little since Miss Pickerel's time:

I remember we used to have 'The Three Ares'. That was 'Are you paying attention?', 'Are you going to get on with some work?' and 'Are you trying to be clever?' We knew the answer to all of them in them days. It was 'No' to all three.

We also used to do reading, writing and arithmetic – they were known as the R, the W and the A. But we done a lot of other letters besides them three. We done R.I. and we done P.T. That last one was my favourite. The boys played football and the girls played netball. 'Course the boys always won, by kicking the ball out of the girls' hands.

In the playground all the girls used to tuck their skirts into their knickers and do handstands. Some of them was so poor that they couldn't afford no knickers, so they din't do it. I suppose that was because they din't have nowhere to tuck their skirts in. I often wondered where them particular girls kept their hankies.

If you was 'never absent, never late' for all your time at school they used to give you a watch when you left. That din't make a lot of sense to me. I mean, if you'd never been late all them years you obviously din't need a watch. They should have given it to someone who was late all the time, like me. Then I'd have known how late I was. All in all I din't get much from school other than education.

23 April, Saturday

How typical of this place! Today is not only our national day, the feast of Saint George, but also the birthday of our greatest writer, William Shakespeare. Yet here there is almost no sign that they are aware of either festival. There is a limp rag, which may or may not be the flag of St George, hanging from the flagpole of the church, but as far as I can tell the day goes otherwise unrecognised outside this house.

I myself invited the Vicar and Lord Silver-Darling to join me for the occasion, and also allowed Miss Pickerel to come. His Lordship was unable to attend, but sent a most gracious apology.

So we were three that sat down to the 'roast beef of Old England', accompanied, for some reason, by a nasty doughy substance that Maud calls 'domplings', which I am afraid to say the vicar ate with his knife. After dinner I gave a selection of suitable readings, finishing with that stirring speech from Richard II, Act II, Scene i: 'This royal throne of Kings ... this dear, dear land.' As a matter of taste I omitted the line about 'this teeming womb' – I fear the Bard does tend to vulgarity at times.

Miss Pickerel paid rapt attention throughout, while Rev. Mullett closed his eyes and nodded in concentration, with only the occasional murmur escaping his lips. Indeed, he remained thus for some time after I had finished, so moved was he. Eventually we had to shake him to bring him out of his reverie. In conclusion, we sang Mr Blake's 'Jerusalem', which Miss Pickerel accompanied on her violoncello. At least the three of us have done our patriotic duty today.

****

In talking about St George's Day in St Just Mrs Prewd was not in possession of one very important fact.

Sid: What she didn't know was that at that time we was still technically at war with England! It was all because of the smuggling, you see. During the Nelsonic Wars, as we called them, the French said they wouldn't supply any more goods unless we agreed to be on their

19

side. So we made a pact with them. We wouldn't fight against them, and if they won then St Just would be the capital of Norfolk. Mind you, that was just a trick, that was. Everyone knows that the capital of Norfolk is an N, and you can't change that, even if you do keep your hand in your inside pocket all the time. Still, you couldn't expect nothing much else from them. The French never was much good at English.

Napoleon was ultimately defeated - twice - and the village kept quiet about the alliance. They cancelled the plan to build Napoleon's Column, which in their practical way they had designed to be both memorial and pigeon scarer. This was a poor idea anyway, as anyone can confirm by visiting Trafalgar Square.

But the village did not forget. Throughout the 19th century they must have been the only village in Norfolk to celebrate Bastille Day rather than Saint George's. The whole matter was not resolved until the 1960s, when the French rediscovered the alliance. Harold Wilson, fearful of what might happen if the village followed the example of Rhodesia and made a Unilateral Declaration of Independence, came to the village for the so-called 'Goat Talks', and a secret peace treaty was signed between the Parish Council and Her Majesty's Government.

St George's Day is now celebrated in St Just-near-Trunch just as it is anywhere else. That is, hardly at all.

Oh hark, the bugle calls my love, you can no longer stay,
For the soldier boys are mustering and you must march away.
'But my toe-nails are ingrowing love, my corns are causing strife;
My bunions are revolting – I can't march to save my life.'

'Oh you must don your breeches love, after you have said goodbye,
For the King he has invited you to go away and die.'
'But my waist it is too slender and my thighs they are too thin;
If I were to don my breeches they'd un-don themselves again.'

And when she heard him say so, she fell down on her knee,
Crying 'Johnny I'm with child by you, stay home and marry me.'
And when he heard her say so he cried 'Alack-a-day,
Bloody wars, the bugle calls my love, and I must march away.'
(*The Bloody Wars* – a song from the Nelsonic Wars)

25 April, Monday

Yesterday I tried to complain to Lord Silver-Darling about the noise, but could not make myself heard over the din of the church bells. Who would believe that the countryside could be such a rowdy place? I had expected that I would miss the bustle of London – the cries of the barrow boys and costers as I trod on their toes, the skirl of the barrel organ, and so on. I never imagined that I should now look upon it as a place of relative calm. Yet here, where I expected at least to have peace and quiet, I have found my ears constantly assailed by every sort of din.

Firstly, there is a cacophony of bird noises. All day huge numbers of the nasty things flap and hop about the place, from the big black ones which emit a sort of croaking sound and look like a ludicrous parody of the elegant ravens which grace The Tower, to the little brown ones, which we have in London, but not in such unnecessary variety. At night these rest and their place is taken by some which I have been unable to see clearly, due to the lack of gas lighting, but which intermittently impersonate the fog horn of a transatlantic liner. Then, as dawn arrives, and one is finally so tired as to believe that sleep might be possible despite them, all the rest return and join in a ghastly chorus which finally dashes all hope of repose.

Then, at 5.30 a.m., the first of the labourers pass down the lane whistling. They can do this at a prodigious volume, aided no doubt by the emptiness of their skulls. Later, they return with great clumping horses, whinnying and snorting. Sometimes the horses echo them. From then on the lane is a constant mayhem of labourers, farmers, tradesmen, merchants and other wastrels. Where they are all going I have no idea. It has occurred to me that they are simply parading back and forth to annoy me, for they manage to make a great deal of noise without any obvious achievement.

This goes on all day long until, at dusk, the ploughman homeward plods his noisy way. But he does not leave the day to darkness and to me. As soon as he has had his tea he heads for that den of vileness, the Goat Inn, from whence he staggers home again at all hours, singing some dreadful doggerel.

But even that is not the end of it. In the so-called still hours of the night men and carts may be heard going past in the pitch dark, on quite unimaginable errands. Once, a loud whisper of 'Stop

21

stamping your wooden leg, Albert, you'll wake the old biddy' was just audible above their rattling. I asked Maud about this, but she changed the subject by suggesting that I watch the wall. I was inclined to tell her that it was not by watching walls that I reached my station in life. I stopped myself in time, however: I am not exactly enamoured of where I find myself today.

****

Unlike today's farms those of Mrs Prewd's time were highly labour intensive. Agriculture had picked up from the slump of the 1870s, when labourers starved in ditches for lack of work. Now they could go fairly hungry in dilapidated tithe cottages. They were happy to find any means of earning a bob or two, and clearly the smuggling habit had not died out.

'Watch the wall' was a local expression which meant exactly what it said. In those days the walls of cottages were often lined with old newspapers, this being the cheapest material available. 'Watch the wall', therefore, meant 'wait until it become public knowledge' – in other words, mind your own business.

26 April, Tuesday

This morning, as the labourers made their rowdy way along the lane to Away Farm, it occurred to me that I had no idea what they do there. For myself I have no interest in the matter, but for the completeness of this diary I felt that I should find out. So I put on my coat and galoshes and followed them, as inconspicuously as I could. Eventually they reached a group of buildings which surround a muddy yard. I use the word 'muddy' in order to spare the reader any hint of the dreadful stench which in fact greeted my nostrils. It is lucky that I inherited my Uncle's strong stomach.

The men crossed the yard and went into some kind of a store, from which they emerged with bales and dirty sacks. These they took to the various other buildings, and shortly there arose a whole variety of animal cries and calls.

At that point I returned home, unable to stand the smell any longer, and mused upon this curious episode. How could any sense be made of these events? I decided to put into practice Mr Sherlock

Holmes's dictum about eliminating the impossible and thereby being left with the truth, however improbable. By this method, the only logical conclusion is that these men are employed to carry bales and sacks into buildings, and then to perform animal impersonations.

A saying of Uncle Wesley's, the one man I have found truly reliable, sprang to mind: 'We are all descended from the apes. Some of us, however, are more descended than others'.

****

This might be the time to say something about Mrs Prewd's uncle, whom she so greatly admired. He had explored what he called 'The Light Continent', where he hobnobbed with Hottentot chiefs, wrestled with elephants, sold his valet into slavery, and so on. It was he who first lost the African tribe which Sir Lawrence Van der Post later rediscovered. But what Miriam Prewd most admired about her Uncle, other than his stomach, was his strength of character. A man who had beaten the Zulu hordes at cricket stood no nonsense from the English working classes. While some found his pith helmet, knee-length khaki shorts and coolie drawn rickshaw a little eccentric in Basingstoke, she thought he was the greatest thing before sliced bread – which, of course, hadn't been invented then.

They were very close and she was broken hearted when he died from a snake bite after a visit to the Natural History Museum in Kensington, but she was determined that his spirit should live on in her, his closest living relative. She always carried in her handbag his unpublished memoirs – *A Straight Bat, and Other Improved Mammals* – and often looked to it for inspiration. I wonder whether she might not have leaned heavily on Chapter Three during her stay in St Just-near-Trunch:

Foreigners
What a chap must remember about Freddy Foreigner is this: he is not British. It's not his fault, of course. And being not British, and therefore inferior, he has his own ways of doing things. Nothing wrong with that, of course, if he doesn't mind changing them to the proper way.
(Chapter 3 – 'Empire, Empire, Stick 'Em Up You Cur')

27 April, Wednesday

As I was enjoying a post-prandial nap this afternoon Maud came into the room and muttered something about an 'old trout'. My hand was halfway to the horsewhip when she hurriedly made herself clear and announced a visit from Farmer Trout, of Away Farm, and ushered said worthy into the room.

There before me was a big, red-faced man, wearing tweeds, a smelly pipe and muddy boots. After placing newspaper on a chair I asked him to sit, but he declined. 'I'll come to the point missus,' he said. 'I'm a forthright man, so I'll not beat about the bird in the bush. Fine words pickle no onions, if you take my meaning. It's all very well for you city folk to go all around the houses, but we country people like to go straight in by the back door. I'm just going to speak out plain.'

I believe we might have gone on coming straight to the point all day, had I not interrupted him. 'Kindly cease prevaricating and state your business,' I insisted, and the sound of a five syllable word stopped him in his muddy tracks.

'Well, it's like this, Missus. I want to know what you was doing hanging around my farm yesterday morning. I don't know what your business there was, but it's none of your business. That land is my land and in future you'll ask my permission to go on it, and I shan't grant it. There, I've said what I come to say, so what do you say to that?'

With that he turned on his heel, grinding mud into the carpet, and clumped out, leaving my pithy rejoinder unuttered.

****

Elias Trout was well regarded in the village, being known as a sound farmer and an excellent player of the spoons. But, like many a stout yeoman, he didn't take well to interference in his affairs.

Sid: He weren't a bad sort of a bloke, for a farmer. We used to call him 'Old Brown Trout'. He had a daughter called Rainbow, who married a bloke from Knapton. Actually, at one time I used to scare his crows. I din't mean to scare them, you understand – they just sort of took a dislike to me.

Anyhow, them farmers in them days could be proper mari-
onettes when it come to their own land. I remember once when a
bloke in a bowler hat from the Misery of Agriculture come to see
Old Trout, and said he was there to see if he could be of any help.
Trout give him a hoe and said 'If you want to help you can go and
weed them carrots.' That's how he was: Trout by name and Trout
by nature.

28 April, Thursday

This morning I sat down with pen and ink, and carefully composed
a letter to Farmer Trout. I let him know, in no uncertain terms, what
I think of his vulgar manners and his grubby land. I had Maud take
it round to the farm and was delighted when she returned with what
must surely be a letter of humble repentance.

When I opened it, however, I found only my own letter with
a note scrawled on the back. Eventually I deciphered this as: 'Farmer
Trout say he canot reed and he canot rite, but he accept yore
appology what he assume you rit about.' I was, of course, appalled:
what a dreadfully illiterate letter. I asked Maud who had written this
frightful piece of prose and she said that it had 'been done' by a
travelling salesman from Ipswich, who was at the farm to sell what
she called 'machines of the devil'.

After luncheon I was visited again by the obnoxious Trout.
'Mrs Prewt,' the farmer boomed at me, 'I have come here to personally accept your apology for spying on me. As far as I'm concerned
the last word has been said and that word is: enough is enough. I'm
not one to bear a grudge, so you can rest assured this is the last you'll
hear of it. I've forgotten it already and I'll remind you of that next
time I see you.' Then, for the second day running, he left my presence
without my leave, leaving me with much to say, but no one to say it
to.

Reflecting on his behaviour over the past two days has
convinced me of the veracity of my theory about the origins of the
animal noises. I would put nothing beyond someone as deranged as
Farmer Trout.

25

MAY 1904

St. Just - near - Trunch Parish Church - a view taken
from THE GREAT HALL   A. KIPPER {Miss}.

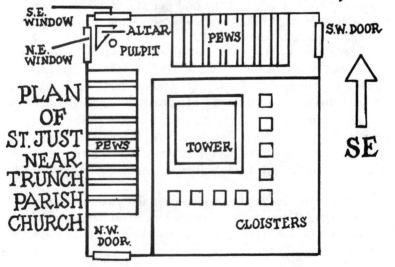

S.E.
WINDOW

N.E.
WINDOW

ALTAR

PULPIT

PEWS

S.W. DOOR

PLAN
OF
ST. JUST
NEAR
TRUNCH
PARISH
CHURCH

PEWS

TOWER

N.W.
DOOR.

CLOISTERS

SE

1 May, Sunday.

I was woken this morning by a fearful cacophony outside the front door, accompanied by much banging and beating on the door itself. On investigation I found Maud cowering under the stairs, steadfastly refusing to come out. Determined to stop the din I equipped myself for any unpleasantness by donning Uncle Wesley's pith helmet and taking up my stout stick. Only then did I unbar the door, to reveal, stood in a rough arc around the step, as ragged a bunch of humanity as one could wish to avoid.

One of these rapscallions stepped forward, bearing an empty sugar bowl, and explained to me that it was their custom on May Day morning to come from Southrepps and call on all the houses around, begging for sugar. I explained to him that it was my custom to give the likes of him a good box around the ears and proceeded to demonstrate the technique. They disappeared soon enough then, but it was over an hour before I could persuade Maud to come out and prepare my breakfast.

****

A brief reference to this custom appeared in the Journal of the Folk Song Society in 1913:

> Perhaps the worst of all the May songs of England is that of the villagers of Southrepps, in Norfolk. It is such a disgrace to the aural tradition that it remains uncollected to this very day. They never sing it to their own folk, but instead rise early from their beds or wherever they find themselves, in order to inflict it on their neighbours in the nearby village of St Just-near-Trunch. The song is part of a local custom known as the 'Asking for Sugar'.

Sid: It was reckoned to be bad luck if you didn't give them no sugar. Of course the custom have died out now. That was the invention of the sugar lump what did it. People learned that you could avoid the bad luck by dinging a few lumps at them with a catapult and pretty soon they stopped coming round.

> All on this pleasant morning from Southrepps come we,
> To beg a bag of sugar to sweeten our tea.
> If you can't spare a bag then a cupful will do,
> And if you can't spare that, then bugger you.
>
> Bad luck to this household, the season begun.
> Where you had ten apples may you have one.
> Now we'll come no more nigh you until the next year,
> And the last thing we'll do is to wish you good cheer!
> (*The Southrepps May Song*)

3 May, Tuesday

Miss Pickerel came to tea and I told her about recent events, including Farmer Trout's behaviour last week. She sympathised, as she toasted my muffins. She knows something of the farmer through his daughter, Rainbow, who attends the school. 'Oh, Mrs Prewd,' she said, for I allow her to call me that in private. 'He is such a rough man, with his dirty fingernails and uncouth manners. Yet the children treat him with such respect. They raise their caps to him and behave so much better in his presence than they do in mine. I don't understand it.'

I asked her whether the children ever made any animal noises and she affirmed that they do little else. 'There is your answer then,' I said. 'They are hoping that when they leave school he will employ them as animal impersonators on his farm.' For a moment she looked at me in puzzlement and then she broke out in a sort of screeching laugh. 'Oh Mrs Prewd,' she gasped between bouts of mirth, 'you're the last person I'd have suspected of having a sense of humour!' Before I could reply she vanished in a cloud of burning muffins.

I have to admit that I was unsure how to reply in any case. She had succeeded in ruffling my poise, a condition quite unfamiliar to me since I told my late husband just what he could do with his stirrups. Who was she to judge my sense of humour? Didn't this jumped up little school ma'am realise that I was once considered quite a wit in Society?

Thinking all this brought on an unworthy bout of self pity for

28

my current distressed circumstances. I dismissed Miss Pickerel, set Maud a few hours work, and retired early, thoroughly dispirited and muffinless.

****

In London Society, Miriam Wilcox (as she was then) was considered to have made a good catch when she married Dorian Prewd, though she was shocked when she discovered his 'little peculiarities'. She bore them, however, as a Victorian wife should, declaring 'A man in his position should be allowed to choose whatever position he wishes, no matter how foolish he may look in it.' In later years she insisted he took his urges elsewhere, telling a lady friend, 'It was getting so that whenever I thought of England the smell of leather sprang unbidden to my nostrils.'

The Prewds were not, it must be said, from the very 'top drawer'. They were more from the 'second drawer down on the right-hand side, next to the hankies.' Their acquaintances were people who were successful in their own right, rather than inheritors of wealth, and in those days it was Earls rather than stockbrokers who were belted. But they did mix with the quite great and the nearly famous, and St Just-near-Trunch must have been a real shock to her. Here was a place where future peers of the realm cavorted in the streets with common labourers and farmers with dirty finger-nails were given genuine respect.

5 May, Thursday

Rev. Mullett called before noon and, while picking his teeth with a matchstick, brought me news of the village. Most of it he might as well have left behind: I have no interest in any births, marriages or deaths which do not occur in the columns of *The Times*. I was, however, interested to hear that Doyley Silver-Darling is coming to stay at the Great Hall again. It seems he has recovered from his injuries and will be here for a few days. He is such a charming man. I think I will invite him to dinner during his stay, though I shall have to oversee Maud's culinary efforts carefully should he accept.

The vicar also told me that Farmer Trout has purchased a great machine from Ipswich, driven by the internal combustion engine, called a 'track tor'. Presumably it is some sort of an engine for making paths up hills, though what use it might be around here I have no idea. Norfolk, as Mr Oscar Wilde observed, is very flat.

Furthermore, I do not understand how such a common man as Farmer Trout can afford what must surely be a very expensive piece of equipment. No doubt he is living above and beyond his means, and I look forward to hearing, in due course, of his inevitable penury following the machine's arrival tomorrow.

****

Farmer Trout's tractor caused great excitement in the area, which is hardly surprising, as it must have been one of the very first in the county.

Sid: Trout bought this tractor 'cause he wanted to show off how up-to-the-minute he was. It was a massive Ferguson and was delivered by railway to Trunch Central Station. The station name was just swank, by the way, 'cause there was only the one station and that was nowhere near the centre.

Anyhow, when they went to collect it they realised that none of them knowed how to drive the thing. Trout thought as how his horseman, Cyril Cockle, ought to know how, but of course he din't. Cyril Cockle din't know bugger all. So there they all were, standing around scratching each other's heads, when the next train arrived. They used to get more than one train a week in them days.

Anyhow, who should dismount this train while that was still standing in the station but Doyley Silver-Darling. When he found out the problem he said, in his lah-de-dah voice, 'I fancy I could drive one of these tractors, Mr Trout.' 'I dare say,' say Old Trout, 'but is this the one?' Well, to cut a tall story short, Doyley Silver-Darling drove that tractor through the village to Away Farm with Herring the butler walking behind with the cases.

The funny thing is, though, that once Trout got the tractor into his barn it never come out again. He said he din't want to get it dirty by using it on the mucky old land. He used to get Cyril to wipe it over with an oily rag now and again, which come natural to him as that's how he used to groom the horses. But he never used it on the land.

6 May, Friday

There was a great commotion in the lane this afternoon and I sent Maud out to put a stop to it at once. When the racket failed to cease Uncle Wesley's adage 'If you want a job doing well you must supervise it yourself' came to mind, and I donned hat and coat to deal with the nuisance.

There in the lane was a monstrous machine, which I realised at once must be Farmer Trout's new track tor. Maud, far from dealing with the disturbance, was abetting it by chattering in a familiar manner with the person at the controls. I stepped forward at once, to admonish him for both breaching my peace and wasting the time of my staff. Thus, for the second time in five weeks, I found myself about to assault the future Lord of the Manor. For it was Doyley Silver-Darling who sat at the controls of the machine, looking rather dashing, with a pair of motoring goggles on his forehead and one leather gauntlet held elegantly in the other.

At the last moment I managed to divert my blow from him to Maud, at the same time ordering her back to work. Doyley looked on, a little startled I thought, and then addressed me in his charmingly refined voice. 'So, we meet again, Mrs Prewd. Must apologise for the damned row, but as you can see I am helping Trout out. I can assure you this confounded din will soon cease.' I, of course, replied that it was of no matter, and that he could drive it up and down the lane all day if he was so minded. Then, remembering Uncle Wesley's advice to always 'drive while the iron is hot' I invited him to dinner tomorrow and was rewarded by his acceptance. At last I have something to look forward to, other than my departure from this loveless place.

7 May, Saturday

Maud was about to serve luncheon when I noticed that she smelt decidedly odd – something I thought I had put an end to with the cold baths I insist she takes. I taxed her with this, but she swore that she had a bath only last week. She was, she said, wearing a locally produced scent called Otto of Rollesby. I told her to go and take it off immediately, with the result that the stupid girl took my words literally and allowed my lunch to go cold in the kitchen. She is only slightly better than useless.

You may appreciate, then, that I was concerned about Maud's performance in the kitchen this evening. However, luck, or as I prefer to think, deserved good fortune, came to my aid. Miss Pickerel happened to call during the day and, when I told her of my forebodings, offered to take on the task of cooking. 'It is the very least I can do,' she said, 'after you have been so good to me.' Inclined to agree, I accepted her offer.

Maud was to wait at table and I gave her strict instructions. 'Remember,' I said, 'that a servant should as far as possible go quite unnoticed.' Being born to the lowest class she should instinctively serve her betters inconspicuously and I trusted that nature would provide where wit is lacking. Nature, however, let me down, for Doyley noticed her almost immediately upon his arrival. As she took his hat and cloak he smiled at her, and said 'Thank you my dear.' I was ashamed that she had made herself so obvious as to leave him no alternative but to address her directly.

Perhaps it was a mistake to have dinner cooked by a school mistress. The menu featured brown soup, followed by a stew of mutton – which was distinguishable from the soup only by the lumps in it – with mashed potato and cabbage. The last course was a steamed pudding with custard, the latter distinguishable from the stew only by its colour. Doyley, however, was most kind about it. 'I haven't eaten like that since I left Eton,' he declared, showing that nature has indeed fitted him with the fine manners appropriate to his class.

Maud let me down a second time when Doyley left the room at one point and I heard him having to speak with her again. I expect he was better able to put her in her place without my presence. That apart, and despite my trepidation and reduced circumstances, I think I may declare the evening a success. Doyley brought me much news from London. He tells me that work is soon to begin on the building of the Panama Canal, following the elimination of the tsetse fly, which would have interested Uncle Wesley, no doubt, as he himself once bit one. Doyley's taste in theatre is, I am afraid, rather low, favouring as he does the works of Mr Shaw and the so called 'operas' of Messrs Gilbert and Sullivan, of which he is inordinately fond. But then, he is a man.

I was sad but content when his carriage arrived to take him home. When I admonished Maud for her shortcomings she burst into tears and the stupid girl did not even have a handkerchief, claiming to have lost it. That girl would lose her head if it weren't so empty.

****

Mrs Prewd may have enjoyed her dinner, but Doyley Silver-Darling did not. Herring remembered the evening because of what he found in his master's pocket:

> One night my master went to dine with the woman from London. 'I had to accept,' He told me as I dressed Him. 'Couldn't think of a damned excuse quick enough.' With this I was ordered to tighten the straps of His truss almost to breaking point.
>
> On His return He claimed to have had a dreadful and dreary time, but there was something about Him which suggested more. Later, as I went through His pockets for loose change, I found a lady's handkerchief. It carried the same perfume as that used by Whelk, the head gardener, and bore the initials 'M.K.'. Perhaps Mrs Prewd's maiden name began with a K?
>
> I decided that I must keep my nose open for any further information as to what my master was up to. A servant, if he wishes to prosper, must go unnoticed himself and yet notice everything.
> (*I Did It* : Chapter 7 – The Sweet Smell of Success)

8 May, Sunday

Maud informs me that today is 'Rotation Sunday'. At first I thought this must be some religious observance of which I was unaware. Fearing I might miss some important office, I went to early communion. The vicar was not surprised to see me, it seemed. 'Very wise, Mrs Prewd, very wise,' he said, banging clods of mud from his hobnailed boots. 'It is best to stay indoors after breakfast on such a day.'

I had no idea what he was talking about, but took it as a warning and remained at home all day, where I passed the time recalling every moment of my dinner with Doyley. I am not sure if I have made this clear, but he is such a fine man, such a strong man. He almost brings out the woman in me, from that place to which my late husband so brutally drove her. If there were only more men like Doyley this world would be a much better place.

At one point this morning my reveries were broken by the sound of running feet and cries of pain from the lane outside. Heeding the vicar's words I parted the curtains the smallest amount, to see a man I did not know being pursued by a number of villagers waving sticks. This hue and cry is the first evidence I have seen of law

33

and order since coming here, and it was all I could do not to rush out and applaud them.

****

The main activity of Rotation Sunday was 'Beating The Bounders'. Anyone who was considered to be a bounder was roused from their beds before dawn and beaten round the parish boundary with the traditional ash boughs.

Sid: How it was done was like this. On the Saturday we all got together in the Old Goat Inn and select a head beater. Then we used to select a body beater, and a leg beater, and so on. That was a proper fair election, you could tell, 'cause the same people got the same jobs every year. Then we used to discuss what particular bounders we was going to beat that year. Now that was hard, 'cause we had to keep the numbers down. Still, we done it, and come the morning we roused them out of bed like you said and set off.

The idea was they got punished in front of the people from the other parishes, you see. They were all out doing the same thing. Sometimes that got a bit out of hand and a bounder from one parish would be picked up by another lot and beaten round their boundary as well. They put a stop to it when a tax inspector got beaten clean across the county.

9 May, Monday

To my excitement a note arrived from Doyley Silver-Darling, thanking me for 'a most singular evening'. I only hope that we may have others like it, making Saturday but one of a plurality of such singular evenings.

But this is neither the time nor the place for word play. I am beginning, dear diary, to find myself attracted to Doyley in a – well, in a personal way. I shall reply to his note as a means, perhaps, of opening a regular correspondence and also to give him an opportunity of returning my hospitality. To my surprise Maud has agreed without demure to deliver my note on her half night off tomorrow. Perhaps she is beginning to appreciate the joys of servitude after all.

34

11 May, Wednesday

This morning Maud looked dreadful. She had great bags under her eyes, indicating that she had been out until very late. Her explanation was that she had to wait while Doyley wrote a reply to my note. It seems hard to believe that such an educated man could be such a slow writer and no doubt she is trying to cover up her own dilly dallying. Since it was her own time she wasted, however, I shall not punish her too severely for its loss.

The note she brought was a disappointment. He is leaving today for London, in order to speak with his Member of Parliament. He wishes to ensure that the man votes against tomorrow's Bill on women's suffrage. How typical of Doyley to selflessly give up his own time to save our sex from the burden of the vote. One can only admire him the more for such an act.

Despite her tiredness Maud displayed today a depth of character hitherto unrevealed. She got on with her work with a will, humming cheerfully to herself – and to anyone else unfortunate enough to be near. I had not the heart to abuse her for it and at one point, while I was thinking of Doyley's handsome looks, actually caught myself joining in. That will never do.

****

The reason for Maud's tiredness – and her cheerfulness – was well known in the village.

Sid: They reckon Great Aunt Maudy had this big passion with Old Oily Silver-Darling, as we used to call him. He used to come up to the village once in a while, and they reckon – well, you know, they done it. Quite a lot, by all accounts. There must be something in the stories, 'cause my father won't say nothing about it and that speaks volumes.

It's not clear what happened to Maud Kipper that Monday night in May 1904. Herring doesn't mention it, although he does say at one point 'His Lordship enjoyed a kipper for His supper,' which may or may not be a cryptic reference to the affair.

19 May, Thursday

I rose just after dawn, unable to sleep longer for thinking of Doyley. Glancing out of the window I was met with the sight of the entire youthful population of the village conducting a veritable orgy in the field nearby, wearing what I can only bring myself to describe as 'traditional Buff'. This went on for longer than my late husband would have believed possible. I called Maud to ask what this might mean only to find her missing. I fear she must have risen early to watch the event, for she returned later looking tousled and somewhat flushed. She explained that the occasion was an old fertility rite, which ensures good crops for the year to come.

In my opinion there is already far too much fertility in these parts as it is. It is quite disgusting that such things should be allowed to go on here in plain view. If the participants had been old enough I should have had them all arrested for the corruption of youth. Instead I went to protest to the vicar about it, but his man said that Rev. Mullett was resting, having risen early for some ceremony this morning.

****

Compared with the sort of things which went on in London at the time, the custom Mrs Prewd deplored was quite natural and innocent. The occasion was known locally as 'the wild mounting time' and clearly dates back to much earlier, pagan days. It's not hard to see the logic of sympathetic magic at work here. The ceremony started with the gathering together of the young people of the village, symbolising the gathering in of the harvest. They then rushed out into the fields in what was known as the 'running out', symbolic of the fact that stocks were indeed running out at this time of year. Once there they removed each others' clothing, symbolising the threshing of the husk from the grain and lustily embraced each other, symbolising the binding of the sheaves. Finally, they staggered home in a state of exhaustion, symbolising the hard work that goes with a good harvest. The act of fertilisation was thus carried out on the very womb of mother earth herself and it was considered especially lucky to become pregnant on this occasion – although it did make it difficult to be sure who the father was.

Unlike many customs this one doesn't seem to have been associated with any particular date. Sid Kipper was uncertain when I asked just how the date of the festival was decided:

Well now, they did say as how you didn't do it until you could bear to put your bare bottom to the earth, but I suppose that was really only a matter of common decency for the girls. Some said that was a question of phrases of the moon, but I can't rightly comment on that, 'cause I don't know what it means. When that come down to it I reckon they just waited until they couldn't stand to wait any longer.

Oh the Springtime it is coming and the girls are in a dither;
Tis the Wild Mounting Time and I am wondering whether:
    Do you go, lassie, go? And will we go together
    To the Wild Mounting Time or will I get bloomin' Heather?

My love is like a swan, with the lightness of it's feather;
But her friend is like a goose and they call her Bloomin' Heather.

If my true love she won't go, then I surely will not bother;
At the Wild Mounting Time I could even fancy Heather!
(*The Wild Mounting Time*)

24 May, Tuesday

Today being Empire Day, as well as the birthday of our good, late Queen Victoria, I had expected there to be a school holiday, as is usual elsewhere. Miss Pickerel informs me, however, that she has been expressly forbidden from declaring even a half day. It no longer surprises me that such an important national festival is ignored in these unpatriotic parts. Clearly celebrating the coming of Spring, as if it were a matter of some significance, is deemed far more important. I thought of Uncle Wesley and what he would make of such a place, and decided that he would jolly well celebrate anyway.

To this end I instructed Maud to run up the flag, but the stupid girl misunderstood and put both feet through it in the process. Undeterred, I went to call on Miss Pickerel after dinner. I have not been to the schoolhouse before and I must say that she has made it rather cosy, in a tasteless sort of way. In particular her display of local china is breathtakingly vulgar. She welcomed me with pathetic gratitude

37

for my visit and threw another text book on the fire, for there was a chill in the air.

When I told her the reason for my visit she became quite enthusiastic and we spent a pleasant enough evening looking through her geography books. We gloated over all the red parts and wondered how their peoples might have suffered without the benefits of civilisation which we brought them. Miss Pickerel did strike a sour note at one point. 'Did not some of these people have their own civilisations before we went there?' she asked. I had to point out rather forcefully the difference between civilisation and British Civilisation. I trust she had grasped the point by the time I left.

****

Empire Day meant as little in St Just as St George's Day. As I explained earlier, the Nelsonic Wars had ensured that Trunch would not join in the celebrations. It's interesting to note that in the village mothers would often frighten their children to sleep with threats that 'Old Hori will come and get you, and carry you away in his arm'. Mrs Prewd must have been a very frustrated patriot in St Just-near-Trunch!

Sid: As a matter of fact someone have just moved into the Old School House. They had to put the roof back on first, of course. Anyhow, this bloke from some village called Islington moved in and turned part of it into a pottery. He's started doing the old Trunchware again, what died out years ago. He does the two bottomed piggy banks and all that. But what I want to know is why does the daft bugger think they stopped making the stuff in the first place? That was 'cause you could get better and cheaper in Woolworths, of course. People like him know as much about life round here as a pig does about Sunday.

They said much the same about Mrs Prewd in 1904!

30 May, Monday

I woke a little late this morning, to see the sun streaming through a gap in the curtains. This was a most welcome change from the dreary weather we have been having, and I was about to throw the curtains asunder when Maud rushed in and cried, 'Don't do it Mrs Prewd, they're coming out.' On looking down I found my nightdress decently secured and demanded an explanation from her. 'Oh, you wouldn't like it if you got it,' she said archly, which, to be fair to the girl, has often proved to be the case.

I could get no more from Maud. When I pressed her she blushed crimson, which cannot have been entirely due to my grip on her throat. She would not allow me to open any curtain or leave the house all morning, during which time I caught the sound of singing coming from the lane. This led me to suspect that they might be perpetrating another of their dreadful customs.

When I did venture out, after noon, I immediately met Farmer Trout. 'Nice out, isn't it?' he boomed and for a moment I could have sworn that he actually had the temerity to wink at me. I am not accustomed to being winked at by any man lower than a Colonel, but refrained from giving him what he deserved because he looked unwell. He has certainly lost a great deal of weight all of a sudden. I told him I would overlook the matter this once and advised him to get back in as soon as possible, lest he catch cold. The buffoon simply roared with laughter and cried 'You're a card, you are, Mrs Crude.' If I am a card, then he is most certainly a knave.

****

Mrs Prewd failed to get Farmer Trout's joke because she was unaware of what had happened in the village that day. The older people had literally come out - out of their winter combinations. The custom is described in Rita Smith's book, *The Place of Underwear in the History of Dance*, Volume XII:

> On a sunny day towards the end of May the villages of Trunch and St Just-near-Trunch saw the annual Wally Dancing. During the Autumn the villagers would have been covered in goose grease and sewn into their winter underwear and now they would divest themselves of it. That done they would blacken their nether parts with a mixture of soot and treacle, in order to preserve their anonymity, and dance through the village, singing the while:
>
> > Untie and untie, and let us all untie,
> > For summer is a-coming in, and we're a-coming out.

39

The custom was abandoned for a period at the beginning of the seventeenth century, following Pitt the Younger's Combination Acts, but revived with their repeal in 1824.

In olden times, of course, the villagers did not wear the 'long Jims' that they sport today. Their underwear was in fact a sort of breach clout and it is undoubtedly this which was the origin of the well-known saying 'Ne'er cast a clout till May is out.'
(Chapter 3 – The Origins of the Black Bottom)

Sid, for once, had little to say on the matter:

I'm not going to say nothing about the Coming Out. Respectable people don't discuss such things and nor do I. I've always held my private parts to be private and I strongly advise you to hold yours the same!

JUNE 1904

Flaming June, flaming June,

Means flaming July is coming soon.

Flaming June, Flipping September,

Blasted April and Blooming November.

All the rest are equally curst,

Excepting February, which is even worse.

(Local saws)

4 June, Saturday

On walking around the area I noticed that many of the flower things are in full bloom. As I took a short cut across what I believe is called a meadow, a rather wild looking man in plus fours of decent quality, if rather tattered, leapt out of the undergrowth gesticulating wildly. 'Watch out for the b.... orchids,' he shouted. Unused to such language, since the death of my late husband, I decided to ignore him. 'You are treading on the b..... orchids,' he persisted, jumping into my path. I treated him to a few of Uncle Wesley's more colourful phrases, concluding by assuring him that if he did not move out of my way at once I would tread not only on his b.... orchids, but also on his b.... foot. This took him aback and, after a while, it dawned on me that here was one of the few halfway decent people I had met since coming to this benighted place.

His name is Fotherskill and he is staying with relatives in Felbrigg. He did not actually say so, but he let me assume that he might be staying at Felbrigg Hall, which is the grandest property for miles around. That in itself is recommendation enough. Anyone connected with that fine estate must surely be the sort of person with whom one would wish to associate.

Percy Fotherskill is a naturalist and he has some fascinating stories to tell about the mating habits of the water snail. Relations thawed considerably when he explained that he had not been swearing at me, but was protecting a plant known as the bee orchid. He also has an interest in the use of wild plants in medicine and says he believes that the common people hereabouts have some unusual preparations of this sort. They refuse to reveal the ingredients to him, however.

The thought that the common folk around here know anything of use or interest is a difficult one to entertain, but I have promised to ask Maud about them on his behalf.

****

Percy Fotherskill came to Felbrigg Hall (now run by the National Trust and a favourite port of call on any visit to 'Kipper Country') following a meeting with Cecil Sharp, the folksong collector. He had told Fotherskill about this area of Norfolk where 'they must know something, but they don't say nothing' – a phrase which was later to be immortalised in the popular song 'Old Man River'.

Sharp noted his meeting with Fotherskill in his own diary:

> I was riding my bicycle around the Northern end of Regent's Park, above the zoological gardens, and musing to myself that this would be a most excellent area in which to have a house built, when I quite literally ran into a man of middle years who was plucking leaves from a variety of trees and shrubs and chewing on them in the way that country people chew tobacco. After mutual apologies had been exchanged we fell into conversation and I learned that he was in pursuit of knowledge of the medicinal properties of plants.
>
> At once I saw a parallel with my own work of collecting the music of the people. I pointed out to him that it was unlikely he would learn much by eating random leaves himself, the more so because he might not suffer from the diseases which they cured. Much better, I urged him, to go out amongst country folk who suffer from all manner of diseases and have been randomly chewing leaves for generations. They must, therefore, have developed some effective cures. I have tentatively called this process the Floral Tradition.
>
> I told him of the strange area North of North Walsham, where I felt sure he might find the kind of thing he was looking for. He thanked me most profusely and was so pleased that he almost danced away in his delight. I jotted the steps down in my notebook, as they seemed to have some parallels with the Moorish dancing of the Cotswolds.

5 June, Sunday

This morning I asked Maud about the local medicines, as I had promised Mr Fotherskill I would. At first she was somewhat evasive, saying that there were no local medicines as the nearest doctor was in North Walsham, which is some three miles to the South. 'I'm going to press you further my girl,' I said firmly. 'Now what do you say?' The stupid girl replied that if she were pressed further she would be lost, as she had never travelled beyond North Walsham in her life. No matter how I tried I could get no sense from her and she persisted in this wilful ignorance until I finally lost my temper, and dismissed her. She had the cheek to accept and went to pack her bags. Realising how hard it would be to replace her I demanded that she take back her job at once, whereupon she asked for an increase in emolument, which I most reluctantly had to grant her. What has become of the self-respect of the working classes? It seems so undignified to haggle over so petty an amount as that which I pay Maud.

What will I say to Mr Fotherskill when I next see him? I have failed to find out any more about the matter of the use of herbs in healing than he himself has been able to glean. I think perhaps my first thought was the correct one. These people know nothing at all which could be of the slightest interest to an educated person like himself and I shall tell him that.

****

Percy Fotherskill never did learn anything of the herbal remedies of the area, although he did discover an interesting local disease, which he promptly caught. He was forced to leave Felbrigg and return to London at once, on medical advice.

Sid: In the old days people couldn't just go to the doctor's and make an appointment for the Monday after next, like they can today. They couldn't afford it, you see. Anyhow, the doctors weren't no good then and most people died of them. So they used to stay at home and use the old herbals – the homeopathetic medicine. 'Course, most of them died of that as well, but they died a lot cheaper.

People often ask me about the old herbals. A bloke come here the other day, and he say 'What's the use of the shepherd's Perce?' I said 'no bloomin use at all, 'cause Perce is the pig-man; the shepherd's Bert'. That was a joke, you see. Bert isn't his real name.

7 June, Tuesday

Mr Fotherskill came to tea, as arranged. We had a pleasant time, and I was particularly interested to hear Mr Fotherskill's news from London. It seems the women's suffrage bill was 'talked out' of the House, so Doyley need not have returned in such a hurry after all. How like men, however, to talk a great deal and yet do nothing.

Mr Fotherskill looked pale and had an irritating cough. He fears he may be ill and is therefore going home tomorrow as he can find no cure locally. I begged him to tell no one that he had met me here and he was most gracious about it. He had, he said, been recently on the Continent and he proposed to put it about that he had met me on his travels there. How generous. How kind. It is a shame that he must leave, but fortuitous that he will bolster my little fib amongst my friends. As Uncle Wesley would have said, 'When one door opens, another one closes.'

****

Wesley Wilcox was a great one for the pithy saying and I think he might have enjoyed some of those from the Trunch area. For this circumstance he might have chosen 'It's an ill wind that has no turning,' or perhaps 'It's half of one and six dozen of the other.' Sid Kipper's favourite is 'When one pub closes another one opens' which, as so often in these things, has its opposite in 'The darkest hour is just after closing time.' Some of the sayings are incomprehensible to the 'foreigner', as in 'Ignorance is nine points of the law', or 'Many a muck heap makes a Michaelmas daisy', but no doubt there is great wisdom hidden deep in these words as well.

11 June, Saturday

I have felt for some time that there is far too much drinking in the village. Indeed, there is far too much drinking in the fields and lanes around the village as well. I said as much to the shy little Curate the other day and today he paid me a visit.

It was as I returned from my daily constitutional – a thing I insist upon whenever possible, as it sounds so like the address of Buckingham Palace. I found Rev. Rudd at my door, trying to pluck up his courage to ring the bell. I feel sure that he would have run away when he saw me, had I not been blocking his escape route. I eventually coaxed him in with a glass of sherry and found that this particular liquor had a remarkable effect on him. Under its influence he became much bolder. I learned that the purpose of his visit was to seek my support for a campaign against the abuse of alcohol by the working classes.

He plans to persuade Lord Silver-Darling to close down The Goat Inn, thus removing temptation from the village. As he was telling me all this Miss Pickerel called and joined us, and we there and then formed a triumvirate which Rev. Rudd dubbed 'The

Temperance Three'. However, before we could decide anything further he admitted to feeling faint and took his leave. As he weaved his way down the lane, singing what I took to be sacred songs and falling occasionally into a ditch, I finished my sherry and felt at peace with the world for the first time since coming to this dreadful place.

****

Ralph Rudd was the youngest son of a once wealthy family and as such he inevitably entered the church. He stayed there for several weeks before his mother found him hiding in the organ loft and packed him off to theological college. There he was too shy to attend any lectures and stayed in his rooms reading the *Church Times* . He passed his exams with flying colours, the examiners commenting 'Rarely have we seen work so admirably devoid of any sort of opinion.'

But he did have one opinion. He firmly believed that alcohol was much too good a thing for common people to appreciate properly and that this led them to abuse it. Just where he obtained this opinion is unclear, but as it was his only one he clung to it firmly. He would even venture into local pubs and offer to save men from sin by drinking their drinks for them. As a result of this he came close to becoming a martyr to his cause on a number of occasions.

12 June, Sunday

In this morning's service Rev. Rudd delivered a very fine sermon. He took a text from the Apocrypha, Ecclesiasticus Chapter 38, Verse 12: 'How can he get wisdom ... whose talk is of bullocks?', but I think that may have been an error brought on by nervousness. Then, for a full forty minutes, he harangued the south-west aisle, where the common people stand, with a most uplifting tirade on the evils of drink. Somehow his bloodshot eyes and beacon-like nose made it all the more telling. Afterwards I asked him how he could so transcend his normal meekness. He told me that he has always found a tumbler or two of brandy to be a most efficacious stimulant on such occasions.

Sadly his sermon seemed to have very little effect. After the service there was the usual undignified charge from church to Inn. However, this is but the first volley of our campaign.

****

It was the first of many volleys for Ralph Rudd. Generally, though, they were destined to miss their target.

Sid: Old Rudd's normal sermons weren't nothing much to write home about. Normally he done little talks like 'The Wages of Sin are Not Very Nice!' and things like that. It was only when he got on to the drink that it got interesting.

My old grandfather was his biggest fan. He only went to that church if he knew Rudd was doing alcohol. He always reckoned there was nothing like one of 'Ruddy' Rudd's sermons for working up a thirst. He said he challenged any man to sit through one of them talks and not feel inspired to sink a few pints straight after. Ruddy was all against the abusing of drink, and so was grandad – he wouldn't hear a word said against it normally.

We're here to fight the brewer's might,
We intend to ban the poison they purvey;
We will bar the lounge and snug,
      where they sell the demon drug,
And have tea shops open eighteen hours a day.

      Are you dry? Are you dry?
      Or are you bound for hell where you will fry?
      We are the little troop who will make the brewers droop
      When they hear our battle cry, are you dry?

Hear our shout; the Inn is out,
The slippery slope is paved with beastly booze.
One sip of alcohol and you will lose all self-control,
And wake up wondering where you got tattooed.
(*Are You Dry?*)

---

14 June, Tuesday

This evening saw the first meeting of our little temperance group. Rev. Rudd, Miss Pickerel and I met at the schoolhouse to make plans and draw up a pledge for people to sign. As the evening wore on we all three felt a growing spirit of bonhomie, engendered, no doubt, by the knowledge that we were doing good to others.

On returning home I was even civil to Maud, which caused me to ponder a moment. There is something very subversive about this business if it makes me civil to servants and gives me a fellow feeling for the likes of Miss Pickerel. I must be careful not to lower my standards with my involvement in this cause. I have begun to guard against it by giving Maud extra duties.

****

The pledges which Mrs Prewd refers to were eventually printed and some people did sign them. I found one still in the possession of the Whiting family, signed by their uncle, Wally. Or rather, it was not signed by him, because he couldn't write his name. Apparently he was approached by Miss Pickerel, who offered him half a sovereign to make his mark on the pledge. He thought this a very fair bargain and signed with a cross.

Sid: That caused a commotion when Wally signed the pledge. As soon as he got the money he took it down The Old Goat and started spending it on drink. He told everyone what happened and he said as how he might not be able to write but he weren't daft. His name weren't Cross so the pledge weren't nothing to do with him.

Everyone had a good laugh at that. All except for this stranger who was sitting in the corner near the dart board. It turned out he was called Colin Cross. And they reckon he never drank again from that day forth, because he thought the pledge had been signed in his name by Wally!

15 June, Wednesday

Further to my thoughts of yesterday I began today's meeting of the Trunch Temperers (or 'the TTs', as Rev. Rudd calls us) by declaring myself honorary president and appointing the others as vice-presidents. This should make our relative positions quite clear. I then called the meeting to order and asked Rev. Rudd to report on his progress with Lord Silver-Darling, whom he had agreed to approach.

It was with great astonishment that we heard what he had to say. It seems that Lord Silver-Darling has been thinking along the same lines as ourselves – or rather I should say more respectfully that we have been thinking along the same lines as His Lordship.

For, whilst restudding the vicar's dog collar in the ante room of his vestry, Rev. Rudd could not help but overhear part of a conversation between Rev. Mullett and His Lordship.

He was, of course, acutely embarrassed to find himself eavesdropping and quickly went to thrust a finger in each ear. However, it took him some seconds to determine that in order for this to be successfully accomplished the fingers must be on different hands. During the time this took he distinctly heard Lord Silver-Darling tell the vicar that The Goat Inn is to be closed. 'The Goat Inn is a thing of the past,' were his very words.

We were so delighted with this news that we celebrated with a glass of brandy, after which Rev. Rudd offered Miss Pickerel a lift home on the crossbar of his bicycle and they rode off into the night with her merrily ringing his bell all the way down the lane.

****

The Old Goat Inn, or as it was then, The Goat Inn, was originally opened in the fifteenth century as The Kid. It was built on the old goat droving road between Frogshall and Edingthorpe, where a brisk trade in goats was plied. Unfortunately building the Inn on the road made it impassable and the goats had to go another way, so it never benefited from the goat trade. But it was used by the locals and the occasional traveller, and did enough trade to keep the Spratt family – the hereditary tenants – in a living.

The Inn was the haunt of smugglers for many years. It also served as a hide-out for the notorious cutwallet 'Gentleman' Jack Kipper, along with his paramour Black Bess, and her horse, Turnip. Another denizen of The Goat was Bald General Coote, who we shall meet later.

It was, for many people, the most important single building in the village, their cottages not excepted. Here they met to mark the passing seasons and the important events in their lives. This was the centre of history, tradition and culture which the Trunch Temperers wanted to close.

17 June, Friday

My heart was uplifted today. Passing through the village on my way home from the Post Office I saw that The Goat Inn has indeed been closed, and a notice to that effect fixed firmly to the door. At least, I assume the notice is to that effect, although it would seem to be incomplete and rather obscure in its wording.

My heart was driven right back into my boots, however, as I neared the main gates of the Great Hall, for there I saw a person from London. To avoid being observed I was forced to hide in a ditch, where, incidentally, I found the water far from dull. This may seem a somewhat drastic action, but I have gone to some lengths to ensure that none of my friends shall know that I am living in the back of beyond and I will not let her spoil it.

She is Miss Ursula Parkhurst the lesser known of the suffragist siblings. As I have made plain on a number of occasions, I will not suffer suffrage. Many is the time I have had violent arguments with that family. Indeed, her mother, Emmeline, once chained herself to my leg as a protest against me. Had Uncle Wesley not spent some time with a Mr Houdini she might be there still.

After Ursula had gone I crept home, dripping wet, wondering what on earth that woman was doing here in my village. Thus preoccupied, I was unable to avoid Farmer Trout, who appeared suddenly from one of his overgrown fields. 'You've no need to go swimming in the river, Mrs Prewit,' he leered. 'You're welcome to come and use my horse pond any time the horses don't need it.'

'If I had my way,' I retorted with what dignity I could muster in the circumstances, 'I would not share the village with your flea-bitten nags, let alone a bath.' 'You're right there,' he replied. 'Derby's the place for fine horses.' As I got out of my wet clothes at home I could only ponder the enigma of his remark and wonder why he felt himself such an expert on the East Midlands. The man is undoubtedly a simpleton.

****

Sid: Old Trout weren't as daft as she thought. He weren't talking about no town. He was talking about the Trunch Derby, which is a horse race. So that shows how much she knew!

That also shows how much she knew calling St Just-near-Trunch the back of beyond. Trimingham is the back of beyond. Trunch is more sort of the middle of beyond. Which raises a question: what right had she got to come round here and say things she knows nothing about? You have to live here all your life before you've got the right to do that.

20 June, Monday

The cause of the Trunch Temperers has taken a terrible blow. The village inn, whose closure last week brought such hope to our little band, has been reopened. It seems that when His Lordship said The Goat Inn was a thing of the past he was referring not to a permanent closure, but to a refurbishment and a change of name. It is now to be called The New Goat Inn, having been brought considerably up to date.

The exterior has been repainted and generally made a fraction less disreputable, but I gather the major changes have been reserved for the interior. I am told – and I have absolutely no intention of verifying this for myself – that the effect has been dramatic. The dirty old beams have been ripped out and thrown away, and the rustic furniture replaced with modern pieces. All the old farm implements and horse brasses, carelessly left there over the years by drunken labourers and, presumably, their horses have been thrown out. The cart park has been dug up and turned into a bowling green, and the weak, light-coloured continental beer which was once favoured has been supplanted by traditional English ales. So I am told. Certainly there are now garish advertisements plastered over the outside of the building, with such slogans as 'Leaves alone the parts that are private.' I have no idea what that might mean.

All of which leaves me with a considerable dilemma. It clearly shows that Lord Silver-Darling actually approves of the drinking habits of the lower classes – at least in so far as they profit him. That being the case I do not see how I can in all decency oppose them myself. Those of us of breeding must, after all, be seen to stand together. As Uncle Wesley would have said, 'Beasts of a fur, must concur.' After some consideration I have decided that I must withdraw my active support from the Trunch Temperers, and I have informed Miss Pickerel and Rev. Rudd of this decision. They were disappointed but have decided to continue the campaign without me.

****

Despite considerable investment by Lord Silver-Darling, the modernisation of The Goat Inn in 1904 seems to have had little effect on trade. This is not surprising, as it had a monopoly in the village to begin with. Ernie Spratt

51

Senior is said to have commented: 'People might notice the difference when they first come in, but by the time they go out they can't notice anything.' This may have been due to the introduction of a new strong ale by the Trunch Brewery, named Old Coote, and based on a recipe previously reserved for the private (and considerable) consumption of General Coote himself. It had a very high Original Gravity and an even higher Eventual Gravity. When I asked 'Young' Ernie what Eventual Gravity meant he said it meant that if you kept drinking it then gravity would get you eventually.

21 June, Tuesday

Maud informed me at breakfast that today is the 'longest day'. I quickly pointed out to her, with the aid of a sharp stick, that all days are in fact of equal length, having twenty-four hours each without exception. I added, to myself, that in this horrid place most of them seem to be twice that long. 'Be that as it may,' Maud went on, 'today is the longest day and the first day of Summer.'

At the mention of Summer a vision of all that I am missing shimmered before me: Ascot; Henley; Cowes. 'I do not suppose for one moment that you even know where Cowes is,' I snapped at her, breaking my cardinal rule of never giving servants the satisfaction of seeing one lose one's temper. Maud drew herself up to what she fondly believes to be her full height. 'I do too,' she said. 'Cowes is up in the top field grazing.' 'Cowes,' I informed her acidly, 'is near Yarmouth.' 'Oh dear,' she exclaimed, 'I must run and tell Farmer Trout at once.' With that, and without so much as a 'by your leave', she ran pell mell from the house.

****

There seems to have been some confusion here. There are, of course, two Yarmouths. One is in the Isle of Wight and the other – more properly Great Yarmouth – is in Norfolk. It isn't clear why Farmer Trout should be interested in the matter, unless of course he was planning to go to one or the other for a holiday.

23 June, Thursday

At the request of Lady Silver-Darling I gave Maud this afternoon off to take part in something called 'June Pole Dancing'. Had I known what it was I would never have allowed her to go, let alone attended myself.

To begin with, men and women danced together in a most unrestrained and intimate manner. Much worse, though, was the 'pole' around which they danced. I cannot bring myself to write here what it looks like. At least, I think that is what they look like, though of course I never actually saw one in full daylight, thank goodness. Suffice it to say that had my late husband been with me it would have put a stop to some of his more unsavoury bragging.

As I averted my eyes from this monstrosity they met another pair, coming in the other direction. These other eyes met mine, looked over at the 'pole', came back to mine, and then one of them actually winked. I was about to admonish their owner severely when I realised that they sat in the face of none other than Doyley Silver-Darling. 'Bit much to take in, all in one go, eh Mrs Prewd?' he said. I could only stammer in reply as I tried to blush. 'Perhaps we shall see you at the races on Saturday,' he continued and before I could respond he walked off.

My eyes followed him through the crowd, till they saw his meet someone else's and walk off with their owner. It was Ursula Parkhurst. My mind was a whirl of questions. What was she to him? And vice versa? Were all my hopes for nothing? What races? I arrived home in some confusion. Maud, when she came in, was able at least to answer the last question. Saturday is the day of the Trunch Derby and I must be there to see with my own eyes just what is Doyley's relationship with that Parkhurst woman.

****

In most parts of the country this sort of dancing was performed on the first of May. And so it was in Trunch, at one time. But in Trunch, as elsewhere, the festivities were banned by the Puritans in the sixteenth century. For a time the ban was ignored, but eventually inspectors were appointed to make sure that no dancing took place. In order to give these inspectors the slip the date of the dancing was changed to 23 June, by which time the inspectors had relaxed their vigilance. The date was retained, even after the ban was lifted.

This was not the end of the tribulations of the June Pole dancers, however. During the eighteenth century Lord Silver-Darling, being short of money, decided to introduce a pole tax. Despite much opposition, protest marches, a petition of over 500 crosses and Lady Gimingham riding through the village naked, he said that there was no alternative, and the tax was imposed. The result was that for a time the June Pole went underground.

Sid: Well, actually it went under the ground. What they done was to dig a great big hole, or pole vault, and bury the pole in it, with just the ribbons sticking out. Then, you see, they could dance round the pole, but the inspectors didn't know it was there, so they couldn't charge them the tax.

     Mind you, that all come to no good in the end, 'cause he put a tax on ribbons after that.

The idea of a pole tax seems ridiculous nowadays, but in those less enlightened times rulers could impose taxes without any reference to the wishes of the people. Today, of course, such a thing would be impossible.

24 June, Friday

Maud greeted me this morning with an impertinently cheerful: 'Happy Midsummer Day, Mrs Prewd.' How could it be midsummer, I asked, when on Tuesday she had claimed that it was Summer's first day? That silenced her and I was able to consider a rather more pressing problem. How am I to attend the Trunch Derby tomorrow and observe Miss Parkhurst without her observing me? One idea which occurred to me was to wear a disguise.

Some might wonder how someone of my natural dignity and authority might manage to disguise these qualities, but they would reckon without my years of experience with the Pimlico Players. We are an amateur company, certainly, but we have had some notable successes with the works of the Bard; successes in which I have played my full part, if you will forgive the pun. I recall that in our production of *A Midsummer Night's Dream* my Bottom was particularly well received. Nor did I rest on my Bottom. I went on to produce a magnificent *Richard III* .

Here, however, I do not have recourse to a theatrical wardrobe. I briefly considered wearing one of Maud's uniforms, but decided at once that these were unsuitable. They were purchased some years ago by my late husband, while on a trip to Europe. When he brought them home I would not countenance them for a moment, but he insisted that in France all the maids wear such outfits and that we too must adopt them if we were to remain in fashion. They are extremely revealing and undignified. Acceptable, perhaps, for the lower classes who have no dignity and nothing of any import to hide, but hardly suitable for such as myself.

In the end I came up with a very clever scheme. I shall simply sit in the cheap seats, which I gather are far removed from the grandstand. If I keep to the back of the crowd I may indeed observe without being observed.

****

The Trunch Derby was first run in 1782, when Lord Derby, visiting the area, challenged Sir Percival Townsend-Guinness to a race. The following year they decided to try horses and eventually hit on the idea of riding them. The two men tossed a coin to decide which of them the race should be named after, and we are told that the gold sovereign was flipped in the air no less than seven times before they got it right. Townsend-Guinness did eventually have a race name after him, though it has now been corrupted to the 'Thousand-Guineas'.

One particular horse, Creeping Ivy, achieved immortal fame by winning the race, against all the odds, in 1853. The odds consisted of a donkey, an old three-legged nag belonging to one Thomas Pearce and a pantomime horse, which actually came first but was disqualified as its back legs had fallen at the fifth. This left Creeping Ivy the winner in a sketch finish, the forerunner of the photo-finish. The owner was so proud that he had the horse stuffed. When it died it was buried in a quiet corner of the race-course.

The only trace of the race today is the fact that The Old Goat still stays open late on Derby Day. As the race is not run, however, no one knows what day this is, so the pub stays open late throughout June, just to be sure.

25 June, Saturday

Trunch Derby Day and Maud was off early to help her disreputable brother curry his horse. I suppose he must have picked up such exotic culinary habits during his travels in the navy. I said it was a shame that his horse should have died just before the race and Maud in return gave me a most peculiar look.

I can now report that today has had a most satisfactory conclusion. I carried out my little plan and had no problems other than those which naturally arise from mixing with the lower classes. By ignoring the smell, the language and, indeed, the people I was able to gain a clear view of events.

The Silver-Darling party were seated in the grandstand, which seemed to have been constructed from two farm carts and a number of beer crates. By the time the horses rounded the final bend even I had been caught up a little in the excitement of the race, but just then an extraordinary thing happened. Miss Parkhurst leapt from the grandstand and ran as if to throw herself under the very hooves of the horses.

One has to admire her courage, I suppose. She might have succeeded, too, if she had not previously chained herself to the grandstand, presumably through force of habit. The whole ramshackle edifice collapsed, depositing its occupants on the grass in a most undignified fashion.

From Doyley's reaction I do not think that Ursula Parkhurst will be visiting the village again.

****

Ursula Parkhurst had indeed blotted her copybook with Doyley, as we discover in Augustus Swineherd's auto-semibiographical novel *Saprise To Cringleford*:

> The disturbance did not reach the actual race course, and the horses continued without interruption. All save Doyley Silver-Darling's prize gelding, Daisy, who took fright, leapt the rail, and charged off across the centre of the course. His father was most contemptuous. 'Damned horse has got no balls,' he thundered, rather unkindly.
>
> Doyley was visibly distaught. 'I had a horse on that pony,' he roared, the veins in his neck standing out on stalks. 'I never want to see you again, Ursula Parkhurst.' With that he turned on one heel, then on the other, and finally stomped off on the pair of them.
> (Chapter 7 – An Inland Race)

Sport-loving readers will wish to know that the Trunch Derby of 1904 was won by Albert Kipper's horse, Red Rum-Ration, at long odds by a short head. The carts from the grandstand were repaired by 'Chippy' Fry, the local carpenter, and Daisy spent the rest of his days pulling one of them.

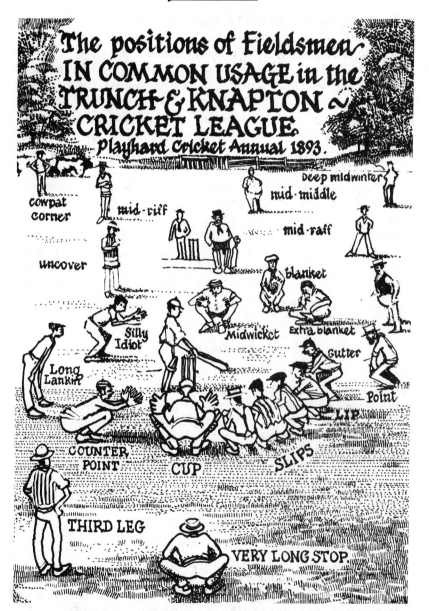

1 July, Friday

My birthday. A lady does not discuss her age, but I was saddened by the wrinkles I observed as I attended to my toilet. I fear that my sojourn in these parts is beginning to take its toll.

I have decided to cheer myself up by giving myself a birthday present. It is one which may do something to improve the appalling moral state of the village. It will make this house an oasis of civilisation in the cultural desert that is St Just-near-Trunch. A desert island, perhaps, such as the one upon which Mr Crusoe civilised Friday. How appropriate, then, that my birthday falls on that particular day of the week this year.

As my present to myself I shall deal with the so-called garden. I intend to have it cobbled, since I fear that paving is beyond the wit of the local artisans, their wit being generally confined to such remarks as 'Lookout, your petticoats are showing, missus.' The uncontrolled fecundity of greenness which besieges me here shall stop short at my borders, unable to gain a toe-hold where I am mistress. In my domain all will be order and neatness, and so shall others see how life may be lived with self restraint and decency.

****

Mrs Prewd's age in 1904 has proved difficult to pin down. My research shows that she had no less than three twenty-first birthday parties for instance, in 1891, 1893 and 1896. Her marriage certificate, dated 1897, gives her age as 24. Her death certificate claims that she was only 43 in 1928. Her birth certificate, which should settle the matter, is unavailable. And the Records Office claim they have never heard of Miriam Prewd at all!

Putting all the information together I can confidently state that on 1 July 1904 Miriam Prewd was aged somewhere between 19 and 34.

4 July, Monday

This morning I waited in vain for my cobbles to arrive. Eventually I had to go and search for the layabouts responsible, only to find them laying about outside The New Goat Inn. They told me some unlikely tale about days off in Looe. What Cornish holidays have to do with anything is beyond my comprehension, but even with my parasol I could not persuade them to do anything before tomorrow.

Meanwhile I have been visited by Mr Clerk, the Clerk of the Parish Council. He tried to claim that I must ask their permission to have my garden cobbled. I quickly let him know, in words he could understand, that I should ask for no such thing. 'What goes on within these four hedges,' I told him, 'is between myself and Lord Silver-Darling.' He continued to mutter about planning permission, however, until I let him know my immediate plans should he remain on my premises. Then he left, still issuing vague threats.

This Parish Council is a classic example of what goes wrong when common people are given power. Their most recent outrage has been to insist that everyone resident in the village must abide by local bye-laws. It has been repeatedly explained to them that such laws are for the control of the lower orders only: their betters are quite capable of judging their own behaviour. Mr Clerk, who is the ringleader of these ruffians, has even served an order on Lord Silver-Darling himself, insisting that he remove the fencing with which he has enclosed the village common. What these fools fail to under-stand is that His Lordship has nothing to gain by this act and must now go to the trouble of keeping animals on the common. His Lordship had the job done merely to provide work for some of the local smallholders, who have apparently fallen on hard times, because of a shortage of grazing.

****

The formation of Parish Councils in 1894 gave the rural working classes a real chance to have a say in their own lives. In St Just they seized this chance, but found that nothing really changed. The enclosing of the common was a case in point. They wrote to Lord Silver-Darling pointing out that if fencing the common had created work for the unemployed, wouldn't un-fencing it create even more work? His Lordship would have none of it and sent the following reply:

To Mr C. Clerk,
Clerk's Cottage,
Clerk Street.

What the devil has it got to do with you? I am the Lord of this Manor
and I will not be questioned by your sort. In the meantime, never
have the effrontery to write to me again.
I trust this answers your questions,

                                                    Darling.

The letter was read out at the next meeting of the Council, held in the back
room of The Goat Inn. The following appears in the Council Minutes:

Mr Clerk read out His Lordship's letter and after some discussion
it was decided that it did not constitute a favourable response on
the matter of the fencing. Mr Albert Kipper suggested putting a
picket round the common, but it was quickly pointed out that His
Lordship had already had this done – indeed, that was the whole
point of the meeting, and would Mr Kipper kindly keep his stupid
ideas to himself. Mr Kipper retorted that his ideas were no stupider
than anyone else's, both in fact and as a matter of principle. He
brought to the meeting's attention the decision of a previous
meeting to put signs on all the local footpads, a spelling mistake
which had led to considerable embarrassment for several of the
Council. At this point Mr Ernest Spratt, who is not in fact a member
of the Council but who, as landlord of the pub, serves a vital
function at meetings, commented that he considered Mr Kipper's
ideas to be stupider than the average, declaring that 'All the
Council were created stupid, but some were created more stupid
than others.' This led to Mr Kipper attempting to dissuade Mr
Spratt of his opinion in a forceful manner, which in turn led to the
taking of sides in a robust altercation. The meeting was finally
adjourned by the Chairman four hours later, when he regained
consciousness.

Incidents of this sort were hardly going to convince the likes of Mrs Prewd
that the ordinary people of the village were capable of looking after their own
affairs.

8 July, Friday

Maud informed me at breakfast that today is Crab Apple Day. I have warned her before about informing me of things without being asked and cancelled her night off. I had to defer the punishment, however, when she explained that she is needed by the vicar to appear in some sort of dramatic production called 'The Crab Wars'. She even invited me to attend, but I declined. The only thing these people can act is the fool.

This afternoon I visited the cobbler to see what was taking so long in getting my cobbles, but could get no sense from him. 'He's only one cobbler,' his wife informed me. 'If you wanted it done quicker there should have been more of him.'

12 July, Tuesday

Today the men came with my cobbles and began to fit them around the house. In late morning I had to go to the chemist's shop for certain personal items which I could not bring myself to mention to Maud. I left strict instructions that the men were not to leave until I had approved the job. I was therefore surprised to find on my return that the cobbles were fitted, but the men had gone. Maud informed me that they had gone for lunch. They had still not returned at 3.30, when I had to go out to tea with Miss Pickerel.

Miss Pickerel tells me that the school holidays begin at the end of this week. She is going to stay with relatives in Hunstanton. 'The cliffs there are magnificent,' she informed me. 'They are a pinky colour and face the sea.' I can think of nothing more tasteless than pink cliffs. The only patriotic sort of cliff is a white one, as at Dover. Her fascination with tinted prominences serves only to reveal once more Miss Pickerel's common roots.

13 July, Wednesday

The gaggle of wretches who are supposed to be working for me were assembled on my doorstep this morning, dull and late. They seemed to think their job was done, but I soon put them right on that matter. 'You must now lay them out in straight rows,' I told them, and set them back to work.

61

14 July, Thursday

Tonight the cobblers were finally finished and I paid off the so-called workmen. After receiving what I thought an exceedingly generous amount, but one which I am assured is the 'going rate', they did not, in fact, go. For some time they shuffled their feet and muttered, until one had the courage to say 'What about a tip, ma'am?' I instructed Maud to tip the spare cobbles over them and they left quickly enough then.

At last I am able to enjoy a truly civilised view from my window. I shall have Maud polish them twice a week.

****

The cobbling of Mrs Prewd's garden caused quite a stir in the village;

Sid: The stones was collected from Cromer beach by 'Ten-Ton' Tunny and Wally Whiting. They delivered them to the village cobbler, 'Piece' Cod. That was the biggest job he had ever taken on and that took him six days to complete. Mind you, he reckoned he could have done it in four if half the village hadn't been hanging about giving him helpful advice. Anyhow, eventually it was finished and by all accounts it looked a real treat. Of course you can't see it today, 'cause the house isn't there no more. My old father saw it when he was a boy but he don't remember it a lot. He was only six months old at the time.

15 July, Friday

Returning from the vicarage at about 2.30 this afternoon I was disgusted to find most of the poorer people of the village had abandoned their work and were spilling out of The New Goat Inn, clearly the worse for drink. I felt constrained to pause and deliver a short homily on the subject of the protestant ethic, but had barely begun with a brief reference to Luther when one of them raised his glass and cried: 'Let's drink to the old coote.' I need hardly say that I did not remain to be further insulted. I gathered my dignity around me and let them know with a single look just what I thought of them and their kind. I left without a backward glance, as Uncle Wesley always maintained one should when threatened by animals or common folk.

****

What Mrs Prewd stumbled upon were the annual Old Soak's Day celebrations, held in memory of the area's greatest hero, Bald General Coote. St Just has produced few heroes of international calibre, so they make the most of the one they have. Coote's greatest claim to fame was that he had been drunk at more major battles than any other British officer, and his day was celebrated, in the way he would have wished, with great gusto.

Sid: They used to say 'Drunk on Old Soak's Day, drunk for forty days.' Mind you, no one ever found out if that was true, 'cause no-one was ever sober enough to tell.

Jane's Fighting Drunks has the following to say about Coote:

COOTE, General Vernon Cavendish ('Baldie'); XXXX, IPA and bar.
Served in a number of theatres and a great many pubs. Mentioned in dispatches a number of times, most notably the Diss Dispatch during the infamous gin-shop trials. His military career was long and undistinguished, having been present at many battles without actually taking part in any of them. According to one contemporary he is supposed to have said that 'the Battle of Waterloo was won in the buffet'. He died in action during a bar-room brawl – ironically his only recorded fight.

Anyone wishing to learn more about General Coote should pay a visit to the Coote Memorial Museum, which is open on the third Thursday in alternate months. It closes for the winter.

18 July, Monday

The village was exceptionally quiet this weekend. There were shamefully few in church yesterday and I asked the Rev. Mullett about it afterwards. 'Ah, Mrs Prewd,' he intoned, shifting the straw from one side of his mouth to the other, 'it is always like this after Old Soaks' Day. You may rest assured that by tomorrow we shall return to the normal hustle and bustle of village life.'

His prediction proved accurate in part. Today there has been more hustle and bustle than ever, but I have been quite unable to rest, assured or otherwise. We have been overrun with children on the first day of their school holidays. Due to the dreadful lack of self-restraint amongst the lower orders there is a seemingly endless supply of noisy, dirty urchins and nobody seems to be in charge of them.

My governess, Miss Trust, always maintained that children should be 'seen, but not heard, smelled or touched'; personally, I would rather they were not even seen. My late husband at one time thought he might have an heir, but I disabused him of that idea in no uncertain terms. I made it clear that I would have nothing to do with children, their birth or most especially their creation. Now, not having contributed to their number, I have no wish to suffer from their existence. But suffer I did today.

It all started with Maud's dreadful brother, Billy, calling on his way to his first day of work at Farmer Trout's farm. 'What noise will you make?' I asked him. He tugged his forelock, as Maud has finally managed to teach him and said, 'I can make any noise I like, missus. I'm going to scare crows.' I told him that he looked fit for the part and he ran along, happy in his own simple way. Hardly had Billy left than there was a knock at the front door. Maud answered it, but found no one there. A knock on the back door followed, with the same result. Then the front. Then the back again. It had to be the brats. 'We'll catch them,' I said. 'You answer the next one and go after them. I'll slip out of the other door and catch them from behind.' Sure enough, the knock came at the front door again and we sprang our trap.

It was only when Maud and I met at the side of the house that we thought to wonder which one of us had a key. So we spent the rest of the morning standing on the cobbles, being taunted and pelted by gangs of children, while we waited for the carpenter to come and break in for us. When he did eventually arrive he simply pushed open the light by the front door, reached in and undid it. 'I thought everyone knew how to break into this house,' he muttered.

****

Mrs Prewd knew nothing of the joys of a country childhood. Her type were brought up within the strict walls of the nursery, where good behaviour was

64

learned from nanny, governess and improving literature. No doubt she spent many hours quietly reading books, such as *The Water Torture*, by Charles Kinsey, full of moralistic characters like Mrs Doasyouredamnedwelltold and Mrs Dontyoudaregetanythingonyournicecleanclothes. Childhood for her class was not to be enjoyed.

Sid: When I was a boy we could more or less do what we liked, as long as we didn't get caught. We used to roam about the fields and lanes, and the like. We didn't necessarily go looking for mischief, but if we happened to find some I dare say we'd make it. Normally there was some older boy who used to say things like 'I don't think your Mum'd like that', or 'If you do that I'll tell your Dad.' We always hated them.

Anyhow, my old grandfather used to do that job till he went to work, which was why they had a bit of bother back then.

24 July, Sunday

On the outskirts of the village is a large open green. I sometimes walk there, for it is a fraction more civilised than the rest of this heathen countryside. The grass is at least kept short, especially at the centre, and there are forms around the perimeter where one may sit. Today, on my way to tea with Miss Pickerel, I thought I would have a few peaceful moments by myself in this little haven. It was not to be. The place was full of men, playing that awful cricket game, of which my late husband was so pathetically fond.

A blackboard announced that the match was between St Just-near-Trunch and Lord Trimingham's XIII. As I arrived a large sweaty man ran up and threw the ball, which one of the batters promptly hit into a nearby field. All the players then rushed off to search for it. So that is cricket. What a futile way to spend God's good time.

Eventually the game recommenced. No one seemed to be over exerting themselves, apart from the sweaty man. Indeed, I noticed that one man on the opposite side of the green had time to receive a note from a young boy, read it and send a reply.

A second glance revealed that this was Doyley Silver-Darling. So I proceeded to walk towards his station, which was directly across from me. I was heartily welcomed with word and gesture by the players, especially when I showed a polite interest by probing the close cropped turf in the middle with my umbrella to see how soft it was. I think they were excited by my interest, though that very excitement, coupled with their coarse accents, rendered their comments incomprehensible.

As I got near to Doyley a man in the middle cried 'Over.' I assumed this meant the game was over. Instead the men all changed places, including Doyley, who strode off to the place I had just left. I was about to leave when I noticed the crumpled note which Doyley had received earlier lying in the long grass. I must confess that I wrestled with my conscience for some seconds. To my shame, however, I succumbed to temptation and retrieved the note. I simply wish to retain it as a keepsake of a charming man.

****

Cricket was very popular in the Trunch area, and visiting teams were often entertained – not least by the antics of the home side in the field.

Perhaps the most famous cricket match in the village was yet to come. In 1931 Trunch played the Burningham team, led by the infamous Douglas Sardyne, in the Bodyline Match. Trunch combated the visiting battery of fast bowlers by wearing the locally made 'Bodyline' foundation garments. To this day, Sid Kipper sings the catchy little ditty written to commemorate the occasion, *The Bodyline Collapso* :

> Cricket, it wasn't cricket, at Trunch where I saw it.
> Cricket, it wasn't cricket, at Trunch where I saw it.
> When Trunch come in to bat
> The bowlers tried to knock them flat.
> Burningham said it wasn't fair,
> They got the runs off their underwear!
>
> With those two great pals of mine,
> Albert Kipper and Douglas Sardyne.
>
> Now victory was completed, Burningham was defeated:
> Though Sardyne he was sour, it was Trunch's finest hour.
> Man of the match, no doubt, leg byes – one forty not out;
> Albert Kipper eased his stays
> And said 'We won it by fair play';
> Sardyne, he said 'No such thing
> 'Your lot had to cheat to win';
> Captain Kipper clenched his fist, and said

'Bad losers make me sick';
Sardyne said did he mean him?
A fight broke out and we all joined in,

With those two great pals of mine,
Albert Kipper and Douglas Sardyne.

25 July, Monday

This morning the village blacksmith called to repair my gate. He is a huge, spreading sort of a man called 'Smithy' Smith. 'Smith by name and Smith by nature,' he proclaimed after announcing himself. I recognised him at once as the sweaty man who threw the ball at the cricket yesterday and asked him how the game had gone. Not that I cared, you understand. 'Not at all well, Ma'am,' he replied, 'not at all well. Very poor batting. Very poor. Mind you, young Mr Silver-Darling scored alright.' I was not surprised in the least. Doyley is an athlete. The rest are clod-hoppers.

When Maud went down to the shops I began to look for somewhere to hide Doyley's note. It would not do to be found in possession of another's correspondence. Noticing how crumpled it was I decided to smooth it out first. I did not mean to read it – it simply happened to be face up. It contained a message in a dreadfully untutored hand. I suppose there is no harm in reproducing it here. The note read: 'Darling, The Prune is out for tea. Get out quick and meet me in the storeroom of the pavilion. Your little Fancy.'

What can it mean? To begin with Doyley should not be addressed as 'Darling' until he comes into his title. And who is little Fancy? I know of nobody by that name in these parts. And what can be so urgent about the tea menu that special notes have to be sent and meetings held?

As I pondered these things, the note spread out before me, Maud returned from the shops and walked in without knocking. She approached me, but then something on the table seemed to alarm her. She blanched visibly and ran from the room. What can it have been? I can only suppose it to be another of her stupid superstitions.

****

That afternoon in 1904 Mrs Prewd was unwittingly honoured to be present at what we may call a great literary moment. It was the incident of the note at the cricket match which inspired that classic of Norfolk literature *The Come-Between*, written, of course, by Augustus Swineherd. This describes, under thinly veiled pseudonyms, the romance between Doyley Silver-Darling and Maud Kipper. In particular it describes the part played by Walter, Maud's little second-cousin, who she always had to take with her for walks and who was therefore in the way whenever they met at some secret rendezvous – hence, *The Come-Between* :

Moyley was not at the crease for long. Young Walker, sitting at the boundary with score-book in lap and pencil in hand, could scarcely believe that his hero was out. Why, the shot was so dreadful it might almost have been played into the wicket-keeper's gloves deliberately. 'Bad luck, Sir,' he piped, as Moyley left the field to a smattering of applause. 'Can't win 'em all,' replied his hero, stopping beside him. 'Cricket's a game for men and if you can't take the rough you mustn't expect the smooth.'

This little private moment between man and boy made Walker's day. He had only one worry in the world. 'Please Sir,' he asked, 'do you know where my cousin Daud is? I'm supposed to be with her.' 'Can't say I do,' replied the young Lordling. 'But I tell you what, young fellow. You stay there and watch the game and I bet you she'll turn up in about half an hour.' With that he gave Walker a friendly cuff around the ear and left. Walker knew that he'd treasure the bruise for a long time.

About five minutes later Walker broke the point of his pencil. He went to the scorer to ask for a sharpener, but Mr Cleric explained that he could not lend his, as it was official club property and mustn't be worn out on just any old pencil. He was most kind about it, however, and suggested that Walker look in the store-room at the back of the pavilion, where he thought he might have seen the club's old sharpener. It wouldn't matter if Walker borrowed that, he said, since it was already broken beyond repair.

And so he found his cousin earlier than predicted. They seemed as surprised to see him as he was to see them! There was Moyley, very red in the face, and there was Daud, breathlessly helping him remove his abdominal protector which, she explained afterwards, had become stuck. How kind of her, thought Walker. She had even removed her own outer garments in sympathy.
(*The Come-Between:* Chapter 7)

AUGUST 1904

If August showers should come your way,

There'll be more tomorrow and the next day.

(Unpopular song)

1 August, Monday

Tonight there is to be a big festival. 'It's the end of the ship sharing,' Maud tells me. I wonder what that means? I can only assume that until recently someone or other has been forced to share a ship with someone or other else, and the partnership is now to be dissolved. It all seems rather odd in an inland situation such as this, but I am no longer surprised by their goings on. Maud seemed to think that I might wish to attend the gathering, but I soon put her right on that score. 'You must make up your own mind, if you can, as to whether or not to attend yourself, but I shall be most put out if you do.'

I was most put out. All night sounds of revelry came from Away Farm and I was quite unable to sleep. Maud came in at a very late hour, singing at the top of her voice something about 'When the lads and the lasses to the ship sharing go.' Using her broom as a baton I taught her a new, more plaintive, melody entitled 'When the Lads and the Lasses from the Ship Sharing Come Home Late.' She is a very quick learner, I must say.

****

Here we have another case of Mrs Prewd's poor ear for the Norfolk accent. What Maud went to was not the end of the 'ship sharing', but the end of the sheep shearing! This was as big an event as the harvest festival. It marked the break up of the shearing gangs, or companies, which would have been formed for the five or six weeks of the shearing.

The following account of shearing feasts of the time appeared in the magazine for sheep shearers, *The Wool Gatherer* :

> The Feast begins with the Head Shearer calling out the traditional toast: 'The sheep have been sheared', which is answered by the company with the traditional response: 'And the farmers have been fleeced!' Then the takings of the gang are distributed according to the rank of each man and boy. After this the ceremony varies according to local custom, but will usually include arguments breaking out over the relative shares received. Then the company will set about the food and drink provided, and carry on through the night, singing and dancing.

> I am a fine sheep sheep shearer, Bruce Breuster is my name,
> And for the bold bush wacking I have earned myself great fame.
> For I've wacked every bush and briar from Perth to Goolagong,
> And after I have wacked them all I always sing my song:
>
> Walsingham Matilda, Walsingham Matilda,
> I wish I had Walsingham Matilda with me.
> And he sat and he sang as he waited till his billy bonged,
> I wish I had Walsingham Matilda with me.
> (*Walsingham Matilda*)

4 August, Thursday

At long last something is being done about the plants which have hitherto grown unchecked all around us. If such an idea were not patently absurd, one might be tempted to believe that the farmers actually encourage them! Now, however, they have begun to set about them with a will. To make matters even better, the children have been dragooned into working all day at the project. I like to think this might be a result of the example of my cobbles.

For some time the tall green stuff has been turning a sort of light brown, so clearly they have found a way of poisoning it. Now they are cutting down the remains with some sort of machinery pulled by horses. Having cut it, they stand it up in clumps all around. Maud tells me that later they will carry it away to 'burns', where they will presumably burn it. She also informs me that this activity is known as 'halvest' – I suppose because it involves cutting all the plants in half.

The whole episode demonstrates once again the shiftless nature of these people. For months they have done nothing about the rampaging growth around them, but now they work all day long to destroy it. Surely it would have been far easier to eradicate it when it first began to appear. My Uncle Wesley always affirmed that unsightly growths should be stemmed mercilessly and early – an adage which applies just as much here as it did to the working classes he was talking about.

****

71

Despite the fact that harvest was the pinnacle of the farming year and the single most important event in the village, Mrs Prewd hardly mentions it again until the harvest festival. At first it seems strange that she took so little notice of the frantic work going on around her.

We must remember, however, that her class looked on all matters involving physical labour as beneath them. To us, in our classless society – where every stock broker is only too glad to roll up his sleeves, remove his Rolex, and pitch in and help the meanest sewage operative – we may find such attitudes distasteful. In those days, however, the sewage worker would have been shocked and disgusted at the very idea.

8 August, Monday

I was returning today from tea and cakes at the vicarage when I saw a huge, rough-looking man with a wooden leg approaching me. Whom the leg belonged to I can hazard no guess, but he was swinging it around his head and singing loudly. I deduced from this he must be Maud's seafaring brother, Albert. On reaching me he called out 'Ahoy there, me russel, I've spliced me main braces' – or as near to that as I can tell. Fearing the imminent descent of his breeches I hurried past and suffered the indignity of this creature calling after me 'I'll pipe meself aboard ye any time you're in port.' I detest the pipes, as my late husband would have told him, and much prefer sherry to port. I shall in future make every effort to avoid meeting this most unpleasant man.

****

Albert Kipper left home at an early age to join the merchant marine. When Mrs Prewd met him he was home on a long leave and enjoying the benefits of life ashore: lack of sea sickness, wine, women and if all else failed, song.

Sid: They reckon Albert was a real wild boy in them days. Well, he'd sailed all over the world – all the bits where the sea go, that is – and he reckoned the village needed a bit of livening up. So he used to drink a lot of rum, show everyone his hornpipe and then do some interesting knots.

72

'Course that was a hard life in the navy in them days. There was lots of beatings. Still, there was lots of beatings at them public schools too and at least the navy paid you, rather than the other way around. There was lots of flogging, too. One Captain found he couldn't put out from Yarmouth at all, 'cause the crew had flogged every inch of canvas.

Anyhow, Albert started off as ship's cook, where he cooked them all the old traditional Trunch recipes. It wasn't long before he got promoted from that to become a Mate, then a Good Mate and finally a Real Pal. He might have gone on to be a Captain, but for the fact there was no way they were going to let a common seaman get any of the good jobs.

In the end he left with an honourable discharge, which puzzled the doctor for years. They gave him a good reference – I believe that was Ecclesiastes chapter 1, verse 7.

To whom it may concern

Albert Clipper is a jolly good chap to have at your side in a tight spot, as he is extremely slim. He has sailed under me these four years – or was it those four years? No matter, he served under me for some four years or other, through hurricane, scurvy, mutiny and war. His cheerful disposition has made him popular with his fellows, though I must say it gets on my pip.

I can heartily recommend him to anyone who is looking for the sort of chap he is.

Signed by my own deck hand;

This thirteenth day of that month;

Captain F.J. R. Hammer-Head

But Mrs Prewd was not looking for Albert's sort of chap at all.

9 August, Tuesday

Yesterday I met Albert Kipper for the first time. I immediately resolved that it should also be the last time. Imagine my horror, then, when this morning Maud announced that someone wished to see me, only to usher in the selfsame oaf. He had made some effort to make himself presentable, I suppose. The bell-bottomed trousers which yesterday had been rolled up to his knees were unfurled, and he had donned a hideous cravat and patched his jacket with what appeared to be a piece of sacking. His cap remained firmly on his head. When I pointed this out to him and suggested he might have the decency to remove it in the presence of a lady, he replied that he had set his cap, and that he wasn't about to un-set it in a hurry.

I enquired after the purpose of his visit, thinking to get it over with as soon as possible. His reply puzzled me. 'I thought you might like to walk out with me,' he said. Why ever he should think such a thing I had no idea and told him so. All other reasons aside it was raining heavily and my dripping visitor was occasionally lit up in an unsettling way by flashes of lightning. He leered at me in what he may have imagined to be a pleasant manner. 'I could try and persuade you to walk out with me,' he said.

I had had enough. 'You could not persuade me to go anywhere without a serious fight,' I told him. He simply shrugged and said, 'Fair enough – I expect we shall get one down at The Goat Inn, if that's what you've a mind for.' This perplexed me, but I had meantime reached into my reticule for Uncle Wesley's pistol, which I remembered I had left there. On seeing this his manner changed abruptly. A horrid leer came over his face and he laughed a loud, sailor's laugh. 'That's what I like,' he guffawed, 'a woman with a bit of spirit in her. You and me'll tack close to the wind before many a sun's gone over the yard broom,' or some such drivel. At that he turned, pushed the door open with his wooden leg and left. I might have shot him there and then, had not Uncle Wesley always maintained that it was not done to shoot commoners in the back, since, being unaware of it, they would be unable to benefit from the lesson.

When I was sure he had gone I slumped into an armchair and wondered what I should do next. Then Maud reappeared. As if nothing had happened she fluffed up the cushions on the sofa. 'I told Albert he was wasting his time with a fine lady like you,' she said.

'But he's taken such a shine to you I don't doubt but he'll be back. He reckon he's a real lady's man.'

I told her to inform her brother that he was seriously deranged and that whatever he thought of himself he would never, in any circumstances, be this lady's man.

****

Albert Kipper did not give up his pursuit of Mrs Prewd easily. For several weeks he would hang about her front door at all times of the day and night, outside pub opening hours. He would follow her up the street. He sent her notes, but she refused to accept them and returned them unopened. Worst of all he would stand beneath her window at night and sing songs. Given what we now know of Albert Kipper's repertoire she was probably saved from terminal shock only by her ignorance of what they were about. These were the real, rough songs of sailors and fishermen – and coarse fishermen at that.

11 August, Thursday

Ever since Tuesday Maud's ridiculous, three-legged brother has been lurking around every corner and attempting to contact me. I have made my feelings quite clear to him with my umbrella, but this only seems to encourage him. It was the same with my late husband. I have asked Maud to keep him away, but her reply was, 'Am I not my brother's keeper?' If she knows what that means I am sure that I do not. What sort of training can she have had at Sunday School to misquote Holy Writ so? I must have a word with the vicar about the matter.

Would that Doyley Silver-Darling were here – I feel sure that he would be able to do something. Indeed, it might even spark a little jealousy in him. In the meantime I shall ignore my unwanted admirer and hope that he finds something better to do.

****

Maud's understanding of the Bible was nothing to do with the vicar. Although she attended St Just's Parish Church with Mrs Prewd, this was not the church in which she had been brought up.

Sid: When that come to religion we was strict Chapel of Rest. We was very regular attenders in our family. Every christening, wedding or funeral, we was there, whatever the weather. Unless it was raining of course.

My old grandfather, Billy, was buried there. That weren't easy, 'cause they had a concrete floor, and that din't half take some digging up. Still, that's where he lies. Well, he don't actually lie – more sort of stands up, really. They couldn't be bothered to dig up enough concrete for him to lie. I often think of him down there when I'm in the chapel, standing below us like that and looking up all the ladies' skirts. I expect he's happy.

The old Chapel of Rest no longer stands in St Just-near-Trunch. It now stands in Knapton, due to boundary changes in 1971. The congregation is ageing and it cannot be many years before there are not enough to keep it open. But Sid still goes there every year, on the anniversary of his grandfather's death, to crawl under the pews and put flowers on the old man's grave. Mrs Prewd, of course, would not have been seen dead in the place.

12 August, Friday

At dawn this morning, which, incidentally, seems to be held at a ridiculously early hour, I was rudely awakened by the sound of gunfire. On looking out of the window I saw Lord Silver-Darling advancing down the lane, gun in hand. Beside him strode Doyley, handsome in the half-light and they were followed by a number of retainers heavily laden with dead birds.

I quickly dressed and ran down to meet them. As I approached, however, his Lordship turned to Doyley and said in a loud voice, 'Looks like we've got a massive bag now, what?'

I have never before been insulted by a Peer of the Realm and I desperately searched my memory for the proper etiquette. What had Miss Trust once said? Something about an insult from a Lord being lower in the order of precedence than a slight by an Ambassador. But Doyley, dear Doyley, came to my rescue. 'A bag is all the birds you have killed and we've killed absolutely masses today; hence a massive bag.'

So it was alright. In fact it was better than that, for at last someone was doing something about the dreadful flapping things. I walked with them to the end of the lane, where Doyley handed me a couple of the dead birds. 'Here,' he said, 'take these for your trouble.' I cannot imagine how he found out about my trouble, but if he thinks that dead birds will help cure it I will certainly give them a try.

****

The twelfth of August was known in St Just-near-Trunch as the 'Inglorious Twelfth'. It was the traditional start of the shooting season – and, of course, the official poaching season. It was the habit of the Silver-Darling family to set out early in the morning and shoot everything that moved, before the local peasantry could get at it. It was said that at dawn on the thirteenth a deafening silence could be heard, as every bird in the area had either left or met its end.

14 August, Sunday

Before I parted from Doyley on Friday I asked if he would like to come to dinner again during his stay. Unfortunately it seems that his diary is full every evening. Tonight he has arranged with his butler to cut his toenails, tomorrow he is having his hair washed, and so on. How typical of the man to be so fastidious about his person. I did, however, determine that he had a small gap in his engagements today and invited him to tea. After a considerable pause, during which, no doubt, that fine brain was considering aspects of the matter which I cannot even begin to imagine, he accepted, and so he arrived at four o'clock prompt. I suppose it is acceptable for such as Doyley to be an hour late.

Waiting with me was Rev. Mullett, who had called round unexpectedly. I could hardly not invite him to stay, once his eye had fallen like a grappling iron on the cakes and sandwiches. I do believe that he would have started on them before Doyley arrived had I not locked them in the china cabinet. Eventually, however, we were all drinking tea and eating cucumber sandwiches – in the vicar's case, three at a time. I could not help comparing the manners of these two very different men. Doyley was sheer elegance, poised with side plate on knee and little finger cocked beside his teacup. The Rev. Mullett, in contrast, was slumped in a chair, a whole cake stand in his lap, and his cup invisible in a vast fist. His presence lowered the tone and I was unable to talk as intimately with Doyley as I would have wished.

I did raise the matter of Albert Kipper and his persistent, unwelcome attentions. Doyley tutted sympathetically, but was otherwise disappointingly uninterested. The vicar, on the other hand, was free with his advice. 'You don't want to worry about him,' he said. 'He's harmless most of the time and legless the rest of it. If he's carrying a torch for you just throw a bucket of water over him. That should put it out.' At that he and Doyley burst into guffaws of laughter and eventually they left together, still laughing, arm in arm. I must confess to feeling jealous of the vicar for that casual intimacy. As I write this from my cold bath I have to say that the event was not a total success.

****

Something was going on between Doyley Silver-Darling and Albert Kipper. That much is plain from Herring's books. What is not clear at this stage is just what was going on:

A few days after the dreadful business of the 'Inglorious Twelfth' my master called a most peculiar man up to the Hall. Dressed like a sailor, he had a wooden leg swinging between the more usual two. It occurred to me that His Lordship's tastes might have changed, following His recent visit to HMS Pinafore. As I ironed his socks I left the door ajar, in order to overhear their conversation.

'You're doing a damned fine job, Kipper,' said my master. 'Keep up the good work and I'll see you alright.' 'You'll see me alright,' replied this Kipper, 'come pay day. 'Tis not an easy job, pretending to be keen on that old bat. I'm not doing this for a lubber like you, I'm doing it for my sister, so you'd better look after her.'

This made little sense at the time.

(*I Did It* : Chapter 11 – How To Handle the Staff)

78

15 August, Monday

The unwelcome attentions of Maud's brother have left me feeling a little below par. Perhaps the fact that Doyley has returned to London has something to do with it, but whatever the cause I am certainly lacking my usual vigour. At least, I was this morning, until Maud recommended some medicine from the local pharmacist, Mr Carter. I must say, they did the trick.

****

The Trunch pharmacist, 'Little' Carter, was renowned for his liver pills, every bottle of which bore the enigmatic instruction 'Not To Be Taken Lightly'. Mrs Prewd later wrote that the pills were 'the only good thing ever to come out of St Just-near-Trunch, after my good self'. She recommended them to all her fashionable friends in London and by 1910 they had become the chief industry of the village. The story of the collapse of this industry following the discovery of the true nature of their secret ingredient is told in the play *Arsenic and Old Lace*.

17 August, Wednesday

At luncheon today Maud had the cheek to ask for a half day. I quickly pointed out that she has only been working for me for four months and cannot expect such generosity for some time.

Once I was certain she had enough work to keep her going for several hours, I set off to pay a call at the vicarage. Rev. Mullett has been kind enough to ask me to call in at any time, but when I arrived I discovered that he had just left. Indeed, I fancy I actually caught a glimpse of him rushing out the back gate as I came in by the front. Rev. Rudd could not say how long his reverence would be gone, as he had 'gone to see a man about a dog collar'.

Whilst hurrying home to catch Maud out slacking, I heard a clanking noise behind the hedge. Curious as to what could make such a sound I walked up the little lane by the hedge and came upon a flat, green piece of ground. A number of men were rolling large, round balls towards another, much smaller one which was painted white. Whatever the purpose of this strange activity they were none of them very good at it, for not one could even roll his balls straight.

Each time they rolled one it departed from a true line and curved around, no doubt spoiling their intention. 'Piteous,' I said to myself.

Or rather, I thought I said it to myself. One of the men, however, had the impertinence to overhear me. 'Reckon you can do better, do you?' he asked, mockingly. I had no wish to get involved with these oafs in whatever no good they were up to, but I could not resist such a challenge and still be my Uncle's niece. 'My good man,' I told him, 'I think you will find that breeding will out.' With that he picked up two of the big brown balls and said 'Here you are then missus, you get a hold of my bowels and see what you can do.'

I instantly saw red over this disgusting suggestion, and he saw stars, I trust, as my stick descended on his cranium. He dropped the balls, one landing on each of his oversized feet, causing him to howl with pain and hop from one to the other across the grass, bringing up divots of impressive dimensions. What happened after that I do not know, for I turned and left at once, arriving home to have the satisfaction of catching Maud cleaning the windows with only one hand. For this idleness I was able to berate her most satisfyingly.

****

Readers will have realised that the word 'bowls' is pronounced in Norfolk as 'bowels' – though how they would then describe someone who actually had pronounced bowels is unclear.

'Skip' Smith, the unfortunate victim of this incident, never played bowls again, although he retained his nickname. Nor did he ever forget about it.

20 August, Saturday

This morning I had a call from a Constable Crabb. Unaccustomed as I am to dealing with anyone below the rank of Chief Constable, especially at my front door, I was about to send him off with a flea in his ear when two things stayed my hand. Firstly, I decided that his ear was probably already infested with fleas and, secondly, he claimed that his business was official. I was persuaded, therefore, to allow him in, though I did not let him go so far as to sit down. Once installed in my parlour he set himself firmly, legs astride, drew out his notebook and launched into what was obviously a prepared speech, which I set out here. You may be sure it is exact, as he left his notebook behind when he eventually left.

> Hello, Hello, Hello. I have proceeded in a northerly direction in pursuit of a Mrs M. Prewd, following a recent interview with Mr Smith of the Garlic Press. He informed me: 'That woman is a real menace, guv, and she ought to be put away for what she's done, swelp me.'
>
> As a result of this and other Information Received regarding Trespass on the cricket field and Abuses of the Parish Planning Regulations (section 3a, subsection 4: cobbles) and taking a number of other Cases Into Consideration, I have come to caution you regarding your behaviour. The Law, let me remind you, has Long Arms and is not to be taken into the hands of those not in possession of said Arms.
>
> You may therefore consider yourself on Probation in respect of your future conduct and we will await Further Developments.

With that he put down his notebook and awaited my response. I gave him a long, old-fashioned look up and down. It was not a pretty sight. To begin with he is only about five feet in height and I should estimate much the same in girth. His uniform was designed for a man of more acceptable dimensions and he wears it without distinction. Around one ankle a bicycle clip struggled to restrain his trouser leg.

Before long I had seen enough and he got his response. The gist of it was that I was not interested in his opinion and that if he could not keep Law And Order in the village, then responsible citizens like myself would be forced to do it for him. He left somewhat abruptly, having failed, it seems, to write a suitable reply in his notebook in advance. By then he was so red in the face that I feared he might expire, or even explode, on my hearthrug. The last I saw was the unedifying sight of his not inconsiderable rump flowing over his bicycle saddle as he peddled up the lane.

****

The arm of the law in St Just may not have been very long, but it was attached to a body with considerably more about it than Mrs Prewd knew.

Claudius Crabb got into the police force by lying about his height. When this was accidentally discovered he was allowed to stay in the Force on two conditions: one, that he remain a village bobby in St Just-near-Trunch and, two, that whenever possible he would stand on a box when appearing in public.

The village constable, then, was an embittered man. He was often to be found after hours in The Goat Inn, with some extremely suspicious characters. But he was not a stupid man, as Mrs Prewd was to discover.

Sid: 'Old 'Claws' was a proper old-fashioned sort of Bobby. He din't throw you out of the pub at closing time, nor stop you getting in, neither. He used to say 'As long as I'm here with you, collecting evidence, I shall know where you are, shan't I?' And if you was to go off to do a bit of poaching he'd come along with you, so he'd know where you were, and that was fine as long as you give him a couple of pheasants or whatever as 'Evidence'. I tell you what, 'Claws' Crabb ate and drank more evidence than any other man alive – though he isn't of course, not now. He was shot in a bank raid in North Walsham, as he was loading the evidence into his bag.

22 August, Monday

I had been expecting an apologetic letter from Constable Crabb, asking for my forgiveness and the return of his notebook. I had most certainly not been expecting him to arrive once more on my door-step, this time with a search warrant. It put me in a pretty predicament. While I had no intention of allowing him to enter my castle again, I could hardly drop the drawbridge on his head, and still claim to be an upholder of law and order.

As I considered this I kept him waiting in the thunderstorm which was then raging, while I painstakingly read through the warrant. I had to admit to myself that it seemed to be all in order. It was signed by a Magistrate of the North Walsham Bench, Brigadier West-Runton, and allowed Constable Crabb to search 'the Premises known as the Old Toll House' for 'Item or Items of Police Property'.

Once I was sure the Constable was thoroughly drenched I handed him back his warrant, smiled sweetly, and told him there was no need for such formality and that I would fetch his notebook down, aware that we were cut off from the world by only the thin canvas of the tent. I told him his future in no uncertain terms, should he not leave me alone from now on. It was not until I made the final point with my umbrella that the sharp crack of a breaking leg brought others to see what was going on. I dare say that broken leg will keep Albert Kipper, not to mention the village carpenter, preoccupied for some time to come.

****

Mrs Prewd is rather dismissive of the delights of the May Fair. But though they may have been too unsophisticated for her jaded, urban palate, they were full of innocent merriment for the village.

Sid: I can remember them. We still do them exactly the same and we had the Fair just last week, so it's not all that hard to remember as a matter of fact.

All the stalls are traditional, you see. First off there's Bowling The Pig. Now that isn't as easy as it sounds, 'cause after a while the pig gets fed up with being bowled. Then there's the plough match – find the two ploughs that match and you win a turnip. And there's an electric thing where you have to get the ring round without touching the wire. Mind you, since my uncle George connected that up to the mains one year that haven't been quite the same. Nor has Tom Bowler, who was the only one stupid enough to try it.

Anyhow, that all go on like that till about six o'clock, when the morris dancers arrive, and we all push off to the pub and leave them to it.

It's nice to think that some things go on the same in the countryside in these days of change. I can heartily recommend the St Just May Fair to anyone with a sense of fun, a bottomless pocket and a good set of waterproofs.

immediately. He then surprised me once more, by pulling out a sheet of paper and reading from it. 'I will, if you do not mind, Search The House Thoroughly as I am Empowered to do by this Warrant. Please Stand Aside.' I was so taken aback that I did just that, and before I knew it he was dripping all over the hall. In order to get rid of him as quickly as possible I ran to the parlour for his notebook, but as I returned I found him going through the hall stand. With a cry of triumph he stood up suddenly, brandishing Uncle Wesley's truncheon.

'Item or Items of Police Property,' he cried. 'And what have you to say about This?' 'This' was a stamp on the end of the truncheon which I had never noticed before. In faint lettering it read 'Property of The Leith Police'. 'Oh ho, Mrs Prewd: I shall have to take this along with me as Evidence,' he crowed. With that last capital letter ringing round the hall he dripped off.

****

Strangely, there is no further mention of this matter in Mrs Prewd's diary. Likewise, local court records show no evidence of any proceedings ever being taken over the truncheon.

Sid: Just like old Crabb, that was – he used to go at everything sideways. He knew that just so long as he held that truncheon over her head then old Prewd wouldn't cause him no more trouble. He din't actually hold it over her head, of course: that was only in theory. But he knew that'd keep her out of his hair, you see. The hair was only in theory as well, 'cause he was nearly bald. There's lots of things in theory. I often think that must be full up by now.

It is certainly true that after this incident Mrs Prewd treated the local guardian of the law with some respect. Perhaps Sid has it right after all.

26 August, Friday

Maud informs me that tomorrow is the occasion of the St Just May Fair. It is to be opened at 3.00 p.m. by Lady Silver-Darling. 'Do you not think it a little late for a May Fair?' I asked her. 'Oh no,' she said.

'It's no good starting before the pub closes.' If I thought she had the wit for it I would say that she deliberately misunderstands me at times.

This afternoon I once again had to run the gauntlet of her terrible brother. Returning from lunch with Rev. Rudd I was pursued by his drunken waltzing and cries of 'You'll be my May Queen tomorrow, won't you, Miri?'

Miri. Nobody has ever addressed me as Miri before and I sincerely hope that nobody will ever do so again. Before long I must put an end to the attentions of Albert Kipper.

****

The St Just-near-Trunch May Fair has been held in August for many years. The reasons for this are not totally clear, but seem to have something to do with the harvest.

Sid: Harvest work is very hard and dry, so I'm told. So the workers thought to themselves, and then they thought to each other, that would be nice to have a day off for wet weather. And then they thought, how could they be certain of having a wet day? And that's when someone come up with the idea. The one day in the year you can be certain of getting rain is the day of the May Fair. So that's what they did. They moved the May Fair out of May, when there was plenty of other things going on to keep folks busy – and plenty of rain, come to that – and they had it in the August. Sure enough, that always rained, so the men had a day off. And the farmers had a good moan. So everyone was happy.

27 August, Saturday

I felt this afternoon that it would be churlish of me not to make an appearance at the May Fair, especially since it is in such a good cause. I decided to go round quickly, spending a little at each stall and then return home. Brevity seemed all the more desirable in view of the terrible wet weather. It was more like May than August. So, with raincoat, umbrella and galoshes, I was at the village green by three, just in time to hear Lady Silver-Darling begin her opening speech. It was difficult to hear much above the howling wind, but what I did hear I approved of heartily. 'There is a difference between "may"

and "can",' she yelled. 'You can do all sorts of things, but whilst I am Lady of the Manor you may not do most of them. That is why I am here to open the May Fair and not the Can Festival,' she added rather wittily. Her speech was ended abruptly, however, by a dripping Mr Clerk, who rudely interjected 'Can we get on with it Your Ladyship?' and cut the tape himself.

I quickly went once round the pathetic little stalls, making my contribution to village life. I was quite ready to go home when I came to the last offering, a rather dilapidated tent bearing the inscription 'Madam Gaga – I See All, Hear All and Speak All'. I had no wish to become involved in such heathen practices as fortune telling and was about to give the tent a wide berth, when to my amazement the vicar emerged from it. 'Ah, Mrs Prewd,' he cried, ringing water from his smock, 'you're next for a glimpse of the future.' Before I could resist he had ushered me in and left me facing a most peculiar creature. It had a shawl pulled around its head so tightly that none of its face could be seen and a parrot sat on its shoulder.

'Now my dear,' the creature began in a surprisingly deep voice, 'what can Madam Gaga do for you? Cross my palm with silver and I will peer into the mysteries of the future on your behalf.' Giving it sixpence I said that I wasn't really all that interested and had only come in at the vicar's insistence. At this the thing cackled, 'But the fates have sent you here, me deario. I see a man in your future.' At this I could not help but take an interest. Could it be dear Doyley that the thing saw? Would he be mine? 'Would you be so good as to describe him for me?' I enquired. 'You will meet a tall, dark, three-legged stranger,' it said. 'Well, not a total stranger. You've met him before as a matter of fact, so you couldn't really say stranger at all. More of a tall, dark, three-legged person you already know.'

My heart fell. The awful Albert Kipper. Was it him that it saw in my future? I tried to pay attention to the ravings. 'In fact, he's not all that tall and he's quite fair when he's had a wash. And what's more,' it said, rising to its feet, 'he's here now to prove the truth of my prophesy.' With that the creature threw off its shawl, revealing Albert Kipper himself, leering from ear to ear. 'Come now, Mrs Prewd,' he said, 'we can't gainsay what is foretold in the stars, now can we?'

For fully five seconds I was unable to say a word. Then I was able to say any number of words. With great control I kept my voice

1 September, Thursday

Miss Pickerel came to tea. She seems to have had an awfully long holiday. How would it be, I thought, if the rest of us left our duties unattended for so long? Where would the village be, for instance, if I simply left for two months to gad about Hunstanton? The lower orders know little of the cares of responsibility.

I am very aware that school teachers are hardly the class of person with whom someone of my background should normally associate, but there are so few halfway decent people here in St Just. Besides, she is so pathetically grateful to be allowed to share my hearth. Just as long as she does not mention the temperance business I am prepared to tolerate her presence.

4 September, Sunday

Sunday, the day of rest, and at last I have actually managed to get some of that precious commodity. The country, in my opinion, is usually more boring than peaceful, but of late it has been neither. With everyone, for once, working hard in the fields and with my recent series of alarms and excursions, I have to confess that my nerves have become a little frayed. Today, however, has conspired to allow me some respite. Albert Kipper has left me alone for a whole week now and it seems that Constable Crabb is going to Say No More about the matter of the truncheon. The work of defoliating the fields seems almost over and even the feathered things have been quiet since Lord Silver-Darling showed them who is in charge. To crown it all Maud has a sore throat and has ceased her tuneless droning. So, after church and Sunday luncheon, I was at last able to enjoy the ordered delights of my cobbled garden. The weather was fine, I had a cool drink at my side and I held in my hands a most improving book.

I have always felt Berk's Peerage to be an essential companion in life, but did not bring it with me here, as I did not expect to need it. It has taken some time to acquire a copy, since nobody in these parts seems to have even heard of it. Except, of course, the Silver-Darlings. I expect they have a copy, but since it was their entry I wished to peruse I could hardly ask them for it. Yesterday, however, it finally arrived from London, and today I was able to find out a little more about Doyley and his family.

What a noble lineage. For generations, it seems, the family have proved their fitness to rule by the single mindedness with which they have bought, fought for, or foreclosed on everything and everybody around them. If blood is thicker than water, then blue blood is thicker still. That thickness is a mark of the Silver-Darlings. My heart was lifted, however, as I noticed that the family has frequently enriched its bloodline from outside the Peerage.

****

Sheringham Public Library does not, unfortunately, have a copy of Berk's Peerage for 1904. But I found much the same sort of thing in its lesser-known rival, Nudds' Nobs:

SILVER-DARLING (Motto: Evil Bees To Him With Evil Things)

The family rose to prominence in the fifteenth century, when Bardolph Silver-Darling sold a horse to King Richard III. With the proceeds he bought another horse. This he was able to sell 'By Royal Appointment,' and the business grew fast. Soon the family graduated from horse trading to the more respectable business of speculation and investment, at which they have had much success ever since.

In the seventeenth century the Family foreclosed on the de Giminghams, and set up home in the parish of St Just-near-Trunch, in Norfolk. The current Lord Silver-Darling rarely leaves there, except to vote against people he dislikes in the House of Lords. His son, Doyley, resides in London, where he is a member of all the best clubs, dines with all the best people, and may be seen at all the best events. He has adopted the personal motto: 'All The Best'. He remains unmarried.

5 September, Monday

Life threatens to become almost bearable. I gather from Farmer Trout that the halvest is almost completed, and the noise and dust will soon cease. Doyley will be at the Hall next week, and tonight

Maud amazed and delighted me by serving up a selection of the most delightful French cheeses.

Previously the only cheeses she has offered have been a rather pallid cheddar or the noxious local 'Stiffkey Blue', which I now allow in the house only for purposes of fumigation. How wonderful it was, then, to have a choice between Brie, Roquefort and a host of others. I confess that I indulged in a somewhat inelegant over-sufficiency.

Having enjoyed this first taste of decent food since my arrival in this miserable district, I congratulated Maud on her provisions. I asked where the cheeses had come from and why they had not been offered before. Maud was even more uncooperative than usual and would tell me nothing at first. After a considerable amount of persuasion, and a number of threats, she vouchsafed that her brother Albert had brought the cheese, and stoutly refused to say any more.

The thought that her awful brother might have touched the cheese I had so recently enjoyed caused a momentary twinge of nausea, but I soon put this firmly in place by remembering Nanny's old dictum: 'What goes down must not come up.' The source of the cheese, however, remains a mystery.

****

The reason for Maud's reticence on the subject of cheese is quite clear – the cheese had been smuggled. At the beginning of this century there was a revival in the smuggling trade which had gone on for hundreds of years previously. All manner of expensive and taxable items were brought ashore at Bacton, and then ferried through a tunnel to the village which, being two or three miles inland, escaped the attentions of the Revenue men. They brought in such things as brandy, tobacco, perfumes and other 'free trade' goods. It was known locally as 'The Chanel Tunnel'.

.   The goods came from France, and St Just-near-Trunch was well known for occasional influxes of onion sellers in berets and striped jerseys. The system worked like this: a letter would be taken secretly to the outhouse of The Goat Inn, which is now, in fact, the Gents lavatory. From here it would be collected by one of the Norfolk men, who would arrange the operation, and before long the cellars of The Goat would be stuffed with contraband, while the English and French celebrated together upstairs.

Close contacts were maintained between the village and their visitors, and inevitably there were marriages between them. Songs such as

'Froggy Went a-Wooing, Oo La La' are still sung by local girls in the school playground, despite the fact that the school was closed some years ago.

Imagine my delight when, on a recent visit to the lavatory of The Old Goat, I discovered that French letters can still be found there! While searching for a penny, which I had dropped the week before, I found a crumpled note, written in French, tucked between two planks. It was my attempts to find out more about this note in particular, and the smuggling trade in general, which led to my discovering the excellent facilities on offer at the Fletcher Hospital in Cromer.

11 September, Sunday

This morning I found out where they have taken all the dead stuff that has been cut down. It has been stored in the church. I arrived to find the place crammed with it, as well as fruit and flower things of all kinds. In the middle of it all stood a great twisted loaf – a reject from Mr Perch's bakery, no doubt.

Before sending Maud to join her ilk in the south-west aisle I asked her if there was nowhere more suitable to put it all. She looked at me strangely and replied that it was only here for the day. What a shame, I said, that it had to be a Sunday. She informed me that it had been brought for the halvest festival, which was about to begin so I must take my seat. I made a note to attend to her seat later, with my hand.

The service, it seems, was some sort of a blessing of the 'fruits of the earth'. Rev. Mullett rose in the pulpit and proclaimed 'All is safely gathered in.' I blushed at what he had to say. It had far too much to do with the fruitfulness and fertility of mother earth for my liking, with much talk of bosoms and even wombs. Such language may be suitable for the tap room of The New Goat Inn, but it is hardly fitting for use in church.

Eventually the service ended, to my great relief. It was only as I went to leave that I saw Doyley Silver-Darling coming from the family pew. He greeted me most civilly and said, 'I trust we may expect you at the halvest supper on Tuesday, Mrs Prewd?' Not wishing to seem ignorant I replied that he might indeed expect me and that I was greatly looking forward to it. As indeed I am. For, whatever its nature, he will be there. Any event which such a man attends cannot be all bad.

****

91

The end of harvest, completion of a year's cycle, was much celebrated in rural communities. Festivals and Harvest Homes are common throughout the country. I had thought, until coming upon Mrs Prewd's diary, that the name 'harvest supper' was a recent invention and that the term 'harvest home' would have been used.

Sid: Well that was used, but not for the harvest supper. The harvest supper was always known as 'the harvest supper'. That saved a lot of confusion, you see. The harvest home was something else. That was when you went out and brought somebody else's harvest home. There used to be a lot of trouble with that round here at one time. People used to put up big notices to try and stop it. You can still see them about today – they say 'Pick Your Own', in big letters. 'Course, no one ever took any notice of them, no matter how big the letters was.

Another old harvest custom was the illegal ploughing. They used to reckon that if you ploughed up somebody else's crop, then you'd be able to get more for your own, due to the shortage. That had to be done at night, of course, as it was against the law. They used to creep out in the dark and if they heard any sound, or saw any light, they all used to run like hell, so as not to be caught. They had a song about it: 'We Plough the Fields and Scatter'.

Another thing about the harvest was there used to be an awful lot of hard drinking went on. The reason it was so hard was because the beer was so blooming awful. The farmers used to make their own at that time of the day, out of the surplus barley, and by the next harvest it had pretty well gone off. They don't do it any more. That's why you hear so much about grain mountains nowadays – it don't get used up for the beer.

> We plough the fields and scatter the good seed on the land,
> But after that things never go in quite the way we planned.
> The moles and mice and magpies come down to eat the grain,
> Before a week is over we must scatter the seed again.
> All good things around us belong to someone else;
> With one accord we thank the Lord and tighten up our belts.
> (*The Harvest Moan*)

13 September, Tuesday

Tonight was the halvest supper at the Great Hall, where they played host to the entire village in the Ballroom. I was placed between Farmer Trout and Rev. Rudd on table number two. To be frank this was a disappointment for I had hoped to sit at the top table with Doyley himself. We were, however, clearly the second-to-top table and had a fine view of those above us.

Lord and Lady Silver-Darling were joined at their table by Doyley, of course, some people called Babcock, some others called Norris and Lord Trimingham. The vicar was there also and began the meal with a grace which I have never heard before, so I assume it is a local one. 'For what we are about to receive, His Lordship expects us to be truly grateful. Go.'

With that he sank his teeth into an enormous pork pie. The rest of the company fell to with equally bad manners and the air was instantly filled with unsavoury sounds. It was like being at a practice session for Farmer Trout's animal impersonators. I said as much to him, but he pretended not to know what I meant.

As we were eating our meal Doyley came over. 'I'm having a little trouble with my speech, Mrs Prewd,' he said. 'Damned if I couldn't use a bit of help.' I offered my services at once, of course. 'No, no,' he insisted. 'It wouldn't do to take you away from your supper. If you would just send Maud to me in my rooms. I shall practice on the girl.' In retrospect this was an odd sort of request, but at the time I was so overcome by Doyley's presence that I thought nothing of it. I called Maud to me and told her what was required. 'Ask the butler the way,' I told her. 'You're sure to get lost otherwise.' 'Oh, I think I shall find what I'm after,' she contradicted. That girl is far too headstrong.

Sure enough, neither she nor Doyley were seen for three quarters of an hour, by which time it was too late for him to make a speech anyway, as the entertainment had begun. I am sure he cannot have been practising on her for all of that time. I expect she got lost and he had to waste his time looking for her. Either that or she used the occasion as an excuse to slip off for a lie down.

The entertainment was distinctly home grown – you may have heard of people making their own amusement. I can tell you that I was certainly not amused. Farmer Trout sang a song called 'To Be A Pharmacist', Rev. Mullett played 'The Organist Voluntary' and

Cyril Cockle did a card trick which didn't work. We were informed by our Master of Ceremonies, Mr Clerk, that the highlight of the evening, an appearance by Jimmy 'Am I Boring You' Kipper, was yet to come. I did not stay to see it, however.

I had not intended to leave early, much as I wanted to. For a start, Maud had not yet returned and it would, of course, have been impolite. The next 'turn', however, was a distinctly nasty one. That awful triped, Albert Kipper, waltzed forward and began to sing a song from the pens of Messrs Gilbert and Sullivan. At least, that is what it sounded like at first hearing. But on idly listening to the words I realised that he was not singing 'Take A Pair Of Sparkling Eyes', from *The Gondoliers*, but 'A Pair Of Sparkling ...' well, I cannot bring myself to write here what they were. Suffice it to say that they were a part of the anatomy quite unsuited for public airing. At least, I thought, dear Doyley was being spared this parody of the work he loved so much. On glancing at the top table I was shattered to see that not only had Doyley returned, but he was loudly joining in.

I could not contain myself. I fled from the room and went straight home. How could he? How could he?

****

Herring tells us more about this incident:

> Every year we had to suffer the harvest supper, at which I was forced to serve food and drink to the scum of the earth. Every year I protested to my master at having to wait on cowhands and swine-herds. Every year He replied that if we were nice to them for one day it might prevent them from turning nasty. And every year confirmed my private belief that it was too late.
>
> One year my master went missing for a considerable part of the proceedings. I managed to get away, and overheard Him talking to His village girl through the open door of His bedroom. 'What a delight to see you, my dear. Only a shame I had to invite that blasted mistress of yours in order to get you here. Still, I don't doubt Farmer Trout will bore her nearly to death,' he said.
> I could listen to no more, as I heard the riff-raff rising from table and knew that I would be missed. I therefore returned to my irksome duties.
> (*What I Saw*: Chapter 7 – They Also Serve)

14 September, Wednesday

It was not until I went to bed last night that I realised that Maud had not yet come home. I do not know when she eventually returned, but this morning she was up as usual and unbearably cheerful. I was still full of gloom and disenchantment. As the day went on, however, this mood was replaced by one of determination. If Doyley Silver-Darling has had a mis-spent youth, then he has all the more need of someone who will ensure that he spends the rest of his life more frugally. He is probably lonely.

Maud, meanwhile, was determined to cheer me up. 'You missed my second cousin Jimmy,' she chirped. 'You ought to go to the Trunch Empire and see him. He's doing a short season there at the moment.' I assured her that I should do no such thing and that I hoped his season would be as short as his wit. I have nothing but contempt for the music halls. They abound here, with the Trunch Empire, the Knapton Colosseum and the Erpingham Majestic all advertising regularly in the local paper. They will none of them have my custom.

****

> I was taken to the cleaners at that Cromer bingo hall –
> I thought I'd lose some dirt, but I only lost my shirt.
> And then I lost my trousers, and my underwear and all:
> Now the world can see how small my assets are,
> And the sailors often hail me from afar!
>
> As I walk along the promenade with a chilly derrière,
> All the girls declare 'My, he's in disrepair!'
> And they close their eyes and wish I'd die,
> They seem to think my end is nigh:
> I'm the bloke who come home broke from Cromer Bingo.
>
> (*The Bloke Who Came Home Broke From Cromer Bingo*
> – one of Jimmy Kipper's songs)

15 September, Thursday

This afternoon two notes arrived from Doyley Silver-Darling. One of them was for Maud and though she would not reveal its contents I can only assume that it admonished her severely for her disruption of Doyley's evening on Tuesday.

My own note was a trifle confusing. Doyley said that he had noticed my early departure and that he hoped it was not the rich food which had caused it. Or perhaps, he suggested, it was the general excitement of the evening. It made no mention of the disgusting exhibition he made of himself, joining in with the absolute filth of Albert Kipper. I was sad to learn that Doyley has now returned to London for a while. I hope that life there has a good influence on him. He is clearly in need of such an influence and I only regret that I shall not be there to provide it myself.

Some people might be surprised to find me so openly critical of a member of the aristocracy. It is generally assumed that they must be allowed to be arbiters of their own behaviour and that as commoners we should not presume to judge them. Let me assure you that my only concern is for Doyley himself. He has so many wonderful qualities that it would be a shame if they were disguised by such peccadillos. He needs a guiding hand in life, and he may be sure that both of mine are here, ready to lead him to the straight and narrow. He has only to reach out for them and they will never let him go.

****

It's clear as the diary goes on that Mrs Prewd was besotted with Doyley Silver-Darling. Meanwhile the object of her desires was having a torrid affair with her maid. It's also clear that Doyley Silver-Darling's tastes were for something quite different to Miriam Prewd.

21 September, Wednesday

Over breakfast Maud assured me, with a perfectly straight face, that today is the 'widest day'. I informed her that it is, in fact, the autumnal equinox. All over His Majesty's Empire – which is to say anywhere of any importance – day and night will be of equal length. 'Well, that's what I said,' she answered. 'It's as short as it's long.' I sent her out to scrub the garden.

As I oversaw her work a most peculiar collection of individuals came up the lane in a sort of procession. They wore blankets, fashioned into crude robes and were chanting something which I could not hear clearly. I called to Maud to tell me who they were. 'Oh, they're the Druids,' she said. 'They're a sort of secret society. I thought everyone knew about them.' When I made it clear to her with my shoe that I, for one, did not know about them she was a little more forthcoming. 'I expect they've been up to the henge for a bit of human sacrifice and an orgy. They like to do that on the widest day.'

I was stunned. Human sacrifice is bad enough, but an orgy – that is disgraceful. I waved my fist at the departing backs of these 'Druids,' and called after them, 'I know what you've been doing and I mean to put a stop to it.' They turned, with surprised expressions on their faces. Then it was my turn to be surprised as I recognised among them Farmer Trout and Constable Crabb. It frightened me to realise that I have all this time been living amongst pagan murderers and orgiasts.

I went at once to see Rev. Mullett, and told him the whole story. He was busy making something called a 'sweetcorn dolly', and seemed quite unconcerned. 'It's just a bit of harmless fun,' he said. I asked him if he considered human sacrifice 'just a bit of harmless fun'? 'Well, personally I don't know what they see in it,' he replied, 'but that's no reason to interfere with other people's beliefs.' I left in disgust, unsure where to turn. I have always thought the worst of these people, but now I know that they are worse than I thought.

****

Mrs Prewd need not have been alarmed. The human sacrifice and orgies of the Druids of Trunch were purely symbolic. What happened at the Autumnal Equinox was very tame. A stuffed straw doll was stabbed with an old castrating knife and then, after sharing a cup of tea, all the participants shook hands. The only thing Mrs Prewd had to fear was the fact that the doll used in 1904 was said to bear a striking resemblance to the tenant of the Old Toll House.

But the henge is a different matter – Flinthenge is a truly awesome edifice. Or it would be if you could see it. On leaving St Just in a southeasterly direction you turn a corner and there it is, below you. Due to it being built in a hollow all those years ago, only the very tips of the great flints are now visible. Originally the stones formed a circle, surrounding a slab of flint known as the Lock.

The purpose and origins of the henge are a mystery. The entry in *The Boy's Book Of Facts And Flags Of All Nations*, 1957, edited by Belinda Dabb, is typical:

FLINTHENGE
In the 19th Century an astonishing observation was made at the stark Norfolk site of Flinthenge. As the sun rose on the morning of the Autumn Equinox it was realised that a single ray fell on the Lock, passing exactly four seventeenths of the way between the third and fourth pillars on the right, counting from the direction of Mundesley. This led to the theory that the henge was used as a sort of calendar, as well as for worship. Of course, this rather begs the question of just how prehistoric man knew when the solstice was without his henge to tell him. And what did they do about leap years?

Which then leads to a host of other questions. How were these vast stones moved from Brandon, where they almost certainly originated? How did they transport these slabs, each weighing many tons, across the flat land of Norfolk? And why? Were they shaped at the quarry or, as some have suggested, napped at nearby Knapton, whose name literally means 'Sleepy Town'? The answers to all these questions may never be known.

Flinthenge remains an enigma. In 1922 one of the stones was excavated by Lord Trawl-Warp, but little was revealed except the graffiti of centuries. Now only the Druidic ceremonies continue and for the rest of the year it lies in silent contemplation, as if waiting for the return of those who built it.

Sid: I reckon the henge was built by a load of people with lots of money and nothing better to do with it. They built it just to show off to their friends. You know – 'Why don't you come over and we'll have a barbecue at my henge?' – that sort of thing. We get a lot of them around here nowadays, converting barns and driving their porches. I don't suppose that'll be long before they start building henges again. As a matter of fact I've got some nice big stones around the back if you're interested.

Since this interview Sid has asked me to point out that he still has the stones and knows where he can borrow a JCB. Anyone wishing to build a henge in the Trunch area should contact him at The Old Goat Inn.

22 September, Thursday

A very red-faced Farmer Trout called today, demanding to see me. Having already received a letter from Rev. Mullett which put my mind at rest about the goings on at the henge yesterday I was not afraid to confront him and had Maud show him to me. This left the burly farmer planted firmly on a sheet of newspaper in the centre of my parlour.

'Mrs Shrew,' he began, thus putting him firmly in my bad books. 'I've come here to be straight with you. If you think I'm trying to be evasive you must say so at once, for I'll not have it said that I didn't put my cards on the table and my eggs in one basket. I think you have a right to know exactly what happened, so, I'm going to come out with it here and now and you must not be shocked.'

At this point my fears of yesterday began to return, but it transpired that he wanted to make some sort of confession related to my shouted remark that I knew what he'd been doing. He thought, it seems, that I was referring to something other than his behaviour at the henge.

'Now I don't know how you found out and I don't want to know – though if you'd be kind enough to tell me I'd be most obliged. Who told you? That's what I should like to know, though I'm sure it's none of my business. My business is farming, unless I'm very much mistaken. Of course, sometimes I am mistaken and this is a case of it. You've mistaken me for someone else, that's what I'm trying to say. I wasn't even in St Just on the day in question, whatever day that was and even if I was, which I wasn't, I didn't go anywhere near Widow Hake's house, unless I was just passing by on my way to somewhere else, which I wasn't. There, I've said it now and I hope you'll say no more about it.'

With that he put on his hat, about turned and was gone, as usual, before I could respond. Not that I would have known how to respond – I have no idea what he was talking about. However, I did get the feeling that I had him firmly on the defensive and decided that that is no bad thing.

✳✳✳✳✳✳✳✳✳

Elias Trout was a man with a conscience. His wife died in 1901, leaving him to bring up his daughter, Rainbow, alone. He used to visit a certain Widow

99

Hake, who lived on the corner of the village green in See View Cottage. Why he should feel quite so guilty about this is something of a mystery, since they were both free agents. But he was an intensely private man, by all accounts, and knew only too well how tongues would wag if people came to hear. As a matter of fact he need not have worried. Everyone had already heard.

Sid: That must have been the worst kept secret in the village. The tongues used to wag every time he went round there, I can tell you. Trout used to visit Widow Hake regular as cockcrow, every Thursday afternoon. You could set your watch by him, if you had one. Which is more than you could say about the church clock. That's been stuck on a quarter to seven for as long as anyone can remember.

25 September, Sunday

It was a special pleasure to be in church this morning. Instead of my usual reception, which varies from being ignored to being talked about behind my back, I was afforded a measure of respect by a sizeable number of the congregation. Farmer Trout, Constable Crabb and others actually greeted me civilly. For a while I was puzzled. Then, remembering Farmer Trout's little outburst on my carpet on Thursday, realisation dawned. They are all Druids and they all heard me shout 'I know what you've been doing, and I mean to put a stop to it.' Who would have thought such a simple sentence would prick so many guilty consciences?

The service was one of Rev. Rudd's temperance tirades. Waving a bottle of gin in one hand he raved and ranted, and roundly abused the whole congregation, giving frequent illustrations by drinking the gin. Eventually he worked himself up into such a religious frenzy that he collapsed in the middle of the church. As the sidesmen carried him out I could not help worrying that he has been overdoing things lately. Every night he has been touring the local dens of depravity, showing their inmates the awful consequences of excessive drinking. Miss Pickerel has spent hours outside some of them, waiting for her crossbar home. I do hope they will take care.

****

```
┌─────────────────────────────────────────────────────┐
│              REV. RALPH RUDD'S ROADSHOW               │
│                                                       │
│  Witness with your own eyes the dire consequences of  │
│  excess indulgence in the demon drink at the following│
│  regular venues:                                      │
│                                                       │
│  Monday      —    The Nelson's Arm, Knapton           │
│  Tuesday     —    The Cricketers Balls, Gimingham     │
│  Wednesday   —    The Jolly Undertakers, Southrepps   │
│  Thursday    —    The Sticket Inn, Antingham          │
│  Friday      —    The Temporary Sign, Mundesley       │
│  Saturday    —    The Dog House, Trimingham           │
│  Sunday am   —    The Crown, Trunch                   │
│  Sunday pm   —    The Goat Inn, St Just-near-Trunch   │
│                                                       │
│  See for yourself how alcohol can turn a sober, sensible│
│  curate into a pathetic wretch, fit only for grovelling on the│
│  floor and leering at your women-folk. Sign the pledge and│
│  leave it all behind you forever.                     │
│                                                       │
│  (Printed for the Trunch Temperers by The Garlic Press,│
│  14 Silver-Darling Street, Trunch)                    │
└─────────────────────────────────────────────────────┘
```

29 September, Thursday

Today should have been a great day for me. It marks, after all, the half-way point of my stay in this hell hole. In another six months I shall be able to return to civilisation. No matter what hardships I may suffer in the future they will be as nothing to those I have endured here. Just six months more.

To mark the occasion I had intended to hold a celebration tea, but unfortunately all those invited were unable to attend, for one reason or another. Lord Silver-Darling replied that he would be calling round tomorrow, but only to collect the rent, this being a quarter day. Miss Pickerel has her parents staying with her and said she could only come if they came with her. The thought of Ethel and Stanley Pickerel passing through my portals was too much to bear, so I had to refuse her. Rev. Rudd declared that he has given up drinking tea and the vicar claimed to have nothing to wear.

Maud seemed unsurprised. 'People always put on their Sunday best to go visiting,' she said, 'but if they did that today they wouldn't be even Thursday best by the time they got here, would they?' After some consideration I thought it best to treat her question as rhetorical, since I had not the first idea what it meant.

****

The third quarter-day of the year was known in St Just-near-Trunch as Mucklemas, as it marked the start of the muck spreading season. Now was the time to put the goodness back into the land and it was done with such enthusiasm that not all of it reached its target. As Sid Kipper put it, 'I shan't say what it was but the air was thick with it, and people who got hit by it weren't exactly fans.'

I can only hope that Miss Pickerel, clearly unaware of the event, didn't decide to take her parents out for a breath of real country air.

OCTOBER 1904

Octave, octet;
Octane, octavo;
Octagonal, octopus;
October!

(Augustus Swineherd)

4 October, Tuesday

This morning, Maud entered to announce a visitor. I told her to show him in, but she said that he would not leave his bicycle. Reluctantly, I went to the door, to be confronted by a figure I recognised. It was Mr Cecil Sharp, the composer and folk-song collector. Luckily, we have never met and he did not know me. Raising his hat, he introduced himself. He was, he said, touring the area collecting the songs of the common people and had called on the offchance that I might know some.

I was stung. Did I appear, I enquired, the sort of person who would know anything of the common people, beyond their sloth, slovenliness and ingratitude? He quickly apologised, pointing out that he had not seen me before he knocked, although the neatness of my cobbles had made him suspect he would get nothing here. He was merely being thorough, he concluded.

Somewhat mollified, I told him that while thoroughness was sometimes a virtue, in this case he would do better to go by appearances. I suggested he go through the village until he came to the most appalling hovel he could find, that being the residence of Maud's relatives, where I felt sure he would discover the commonest of people and, presumably, their common songs.

He thanked me, and said he would try my method. I last saw him wobbling up the lane on his bicycle, singing at the top of his voice something that sounded like 'Do you know Ken Peel?'

****

For a while folk-song collecting was all the rage amongst the upper-middle classes. Villages like St Just were besieged by collectors, looking for previously undiscovered songs. Of course, it was only the upper-middle classes who could discover such material – the ordinary people of the towns and villages of England had never lost it.

The Kipper family, with their reputation for singing, were frequently called on, although they never gave their songs to collectors, preferring to keep them for their own use.

Sid: At one time you couldn't hardly move in The Goat Inn for folk-song collectors. They'd all be in there, practising collecting songs off each other and trying to get the locals to sing for them. That Cecil

Sharp he was the worst one. He used to collect all these songs and then cut out the dirty bits. He put what was left in a book and kept all the dirty bits for himself.

They used to come round the house. Cecil Sharp, he come round twice. The first time he come he saw my old grandfather, Billy, who told him to bugger off. He didn't want his dirty bits cutting out, you see. He was proud of his dirty bits, was old Billy. But Sharp didn't give up. He come round again a couple of days later, when grandfather was out, and saw my old great uncle Albert. He say to Albert, 'have you got any old folk-songs you don't want?'

Well, Albert looked him straight in the eye. 'I'm not really sure what you mean, Mr Sharp,' he said finally. 'Can you sing me one as an example?' So Sharp sung him this song, and then he said, 'Now do you see the sort of thing I mean, Mr Kipper?' Uncle Albert thought about that and scratched his head. 'No, I'm still not clear,' he said. 'Will you sing it for me again?'

Well, to cut a long story down to size, Cecil Sharp sung him this song three or four times. After the third or fourth time he asked Albert, 'Now do you see the sort of thing I mean?' 'Oh yes,' said Albert, 'I see exactly the sort of thing you mean now.' 'Well,' say Sharp, 'have you got any old songs like that?' 'As a matter of fact,' said Albert, 'no, we haven't.'

But the interesting thing about it all is that that's how my old uncle Albert became the only person in history that ever collected a song from Cecil Sharp! Mind you, that weren't much of a song, 'cause that hadn't no dirty bits in and what's an old folk-song without its dirty bits?

Oftimes they sing about the hardships of a farmer's life,
But little do we hear about the poor old farmer's wife;
For he must rise at five o'clock to go to his cow shed,
But she must rise at half-past four to bring him tea in bed.

> I can cook, I can sew, I can sweep, I can mow,
> And at dinners I am a real charmer;
> But jolly girls all, pay heed to my call,
> God help you if you marry a farmer.

(*The Farmers Crumpet*, collected from Cecil Sharp)

---

7 October, Friday

This morning I received a letter from London. While this might seem only natural, its arrival caused me some consternation. Remember, my exile here is supposed to be a secret from all but Mr Penguin and this letter was not addressed in his characteristic silver-plate writing. Had Mr Sharp recognised me after all and given me away? It was with some trepidation that I opened the envelope and perused its contents.

I need not have worried. Indeed, I was delighted. It was from Doyley Silver-Darling. He enthused about the theatre and ended by inviting himself here after dinner on Monday, finishing:

> We could have a jolly quiet evening together, my dear old thing, and I could bring you all the news from London. We would be more alone if you gave that maid of yours the night off, don't you think? Reply to the Hall and leave the rest to me.

I was overjoyed. To think that Doyley has been thinking of me whilst in London. I had some difficulty in framing my reply. Decent society, after all, is based upon formal invitations and acceptances, but as Doyley has invited himself I could hardly send an acceptance. Nor could I send an invitation. The only other sort of formal message would be one of condolence, but that seemed somewhat inappropriate. Eventually I settled on a compromise and sent a birthday card with the message, 'Looking forward to your company on Monday – Maud will have the night off.'

I hope he will understand. I cannot wait until Monday, and yet I must.

8 October, Saturday

What a long day this has seemed. I have been able to think of little else but Monday's meeting with Doyley. I do hope I am not building my hopes too high. As I read and reread his letter I thrill especially to his calling me his 'dear old thing'. Whilst the term 'old' and 'thing' might, if taken literally, be considered rather unflattering, they are nevertheless worth it for the 'dear'. I take the whole phrase to be a term of endearment.

As to his suggestion that I send Maud away for the night, what can he have in mind? Nothing dishonourable, I am sure. I will give Maud the night off, but will not tell her anything about it yet. She would only worry about what to do. She is forever fretting over what to do with her spare time, and often says that she would like to do so-and-so and so-and-so but can only do one of them, and cannot make up her mind which. When I suggest the obvious solution to her dilemma – that she work through her time off and save herself the difficulty of choosing – she invariably decides there and then which is the more important. I am sure she does this simply to annoy me, but with Monday in prospect I am not going to let her do so on this occasion.

9 October, Sunday

How this weekend has dragged. I have been wondering, what does Doyley mean by a 'jolly quiet evening'? Does he mean an evening that is both jolly and quiet, or does he mean one that is extremely quiet? By all means I am quite ready to be quietly jolly or, indeed, very quiet, but what should we be doing during all that quietness, and how will I know whether to be jolly or not?

I know that I have only to wait for the morrow, but the morrow seems so long in coming.

10 October, Monday

Today the morrow finally came, but it brought a terrible disappointment.

It all happened in a rather peculiar way. As the appointed hour approached I called Maud in, and told her that she might go and spend the night with her family. I had anticipated that she would be gratefully surprised, but she reacted almost as though she had been expecting it. She picked up a bag, which seemed to have been already packed and left. Only seconds later there was a knock at the door and my heart leapt. On opening the door, however, I found not Doyley but his coachman. 'Note from his Lordship,' he announced curtly and departed. I quickly read the note, which said that Doyley had a headache and could not come. I ran down the path, hoping to send a reply, or even to catch Maud and set her some useful work to do. I was too late. The coach was already turning at the end of the lane and although the light was not good, I could have sworn I saw two figures riding in the back of it.

11 October, Tuesday

Following my disappointment last evening I decided I must do something to cheer myself up. Unfortunately the best I could arrange at short notice was to invite Miss Pickerel out to tea. She accepted gladly, and we set off together to Mrs Dace's Corner Emporium and Tea Rooms. Here we had the rather dubious pleasure of tea, crumpet and scones.

Miss Pickerel was full of prattle. She brought me up to date on the temperance campaign and bemoaned the shortcomings of her pupils. They are capable of little, it seems, which hardly surprises me. They struggle, according to Miss Pickerel, with even simple things. Not one of them, for instance, can read a word of Latin.

I find this comforting. To what use would the common people put education? To get up to no good, is my belief. Teach them to write and what would they do? They would write and complain. Teach them to count and they would want more wages. Teach them to think and there is no saying what might happen. I pointed this out to Miss Pickerel and begged her not to teach them anything which might unsettle their simple lives. She laughed, saying there was very little chance of that.

We passed the afternoon in pleasant enough conversation, until the time came for us to go. It was then that Miss Pickerel revealed her true colours. When the bill arrived she steadfastly failed to offer to pay. As you may see, this robbed me of the chance to insist that she must not and therefore the pleasure of enjoying my patronage of her. I fear that she is forgetting her place. At an appropriate time I must take the opportunity of putting her firmly in it.

****

It's hard for us nowadays to fully appreciate the importance of social status in a remote village in Edwardian England. Yet Mrs Prewd worried about it constantly, perhaps because she did not fit easily into the system. She does seem to have slipped up in taking tea in public with a school teacher. Mrs Dace would surely have commented on it. She was a stickler for social correctness amongst her customers.

Sid: One time she threw the vicar out for eating peas off his knife which weren't really fair 'cause she hadn't given him a fork, on account of the previous time he'd used it in the wrong hand. Another time she threw a travelling salesman out on one ear for picking the other one.

But most of all she worried about people knowing their places. For the poshest people their place was in the window, so they could be seen. For ordinary teashop sort of people, like school teachers, their place was at the back of the room, where you had people pushing past you all the time to get to what she called 'the facilities'.

Mrs Dace's granddaughter, Mrs Dace, still runs the corner shop and tea rooms. Her artificial cream teas are much in demand, and I have often refreshed myself there with a pot of something warm and wet. Unfortunately I've never managed to make it clear that I would prefer tea.

13 October, Thursday

Today I paid a call in Knapton. Normally, of course, I would not go near the place, but I had to visit someone there on a rather delicate matter.

At first I had thought my hearing was failing. Rev. Mullett, however, reassured me. 'It is the accent, Mrs Prewd. You do not need a doctor, but an elocutionist.' I sharply pointed out that my diction is of the highest class, having been coached by the finest English teacher in London, Monsieur Heinrich Garibaldi. 'I fear you misunderstand me, Mrs Prewd,' he said. 'I misunderstand far too many people in these parts, vicar,' I replied. 'That is the problem.' So today, on his advice, I went to Knapton to visit Mrs Mathews.

Elizabeth Mathews lives in a neat little cottage called 'Gilwell'. I asked her about this rather odd name. 'Well, what would you call it?' she replied, to which I must confess I could find no answer. Her time, it seems, is precious – it is certainly expensive – and she insisted that we 'get on with it', as she put it, 'at once'. So I explained to her the incident of the soup.

It happened when I first came here and had just engaged Maud. She came to me one day and announced that she was going to the shop for some 'toilet soup'. I thought she had gone mad or was intending to poison me, and forbad her to buy any. Later that evening, as I went to wash my face, I could find nothing to wash it with. Eventually I roused Maud from the broom cupboard and demanded to know what was going on. 'But you told me I wasn't to go for no soup,' she pleaded. How was I to know that the heathen tongue of these parts renders 'soap' as 'soup'?

There have been countless other examples since then. There was the business of the 'bowels'. There was the day when Farmer Trout alarmed me by announcing that he was 'darned if he weren't going to get his dicky out for a bit of air' – a dicky, it transpired, being a local word for a donkey. And how is it that if a 'boot' is a boat, 'bootiful' is beautiful?

Mrs Mathews was wonderful. She suffers no nonsense, and soon had me hearing what was meant. As Uncle Wesley used to say: 'If you can't beat them, thrash them!' It was a triumph of intelligence over ignorance. The natives are too ignorant to speak clearly, so I must use my intelligence to understand them. Next time I call Mr Dace a bore I shall be sure that he knows exactly what I mean.

****

The Norfolk accent is a difficult one to master. It wasn't in Mrs Prewd's nature, however, to be defeated by a mere difficulty. More to the point, it wasn't in her nature to allow someone to insult her without her knowing it, as she feared they might. For four Thursdays she visited 'Gilwell'. Mrs Mathews, being a conscientious teacher, kept full notes on her pupil and these throw an interesting sidelight on our diarist.

October 13th: Mrs Prewd came for her first lesson today. She is a stiff-necked woman and extremely overbearing. No matter – I shall be overcharging.

October 20th: I actually feel a bit sorry for Mrs Prewd. She is 'lonely in the crowd', so to speak. There are very few people in her village who she deigns to talk with, and when she does she cannot understand half of what they say. Still, it will not take long to help her. I could do it in an hour, but will make it last for another three.

110

October 27th:	She is a determined and able pupil. She has mastered the 'oo' and is now coping well with the grammar. There is only the vocabulary to go.
November 3rd:	Mrs Prewd did not arrive today. The bill will reflect my annoyance.
November 10th:	I am rather proud of my pupil. She can now under stand what people are saying. I only hope she can bear to hear some of the things they are saying about her!
November 20th:	Bill paid; case closed.

> When we have a do then the grass is all wet;
> A thud's one divided by three;
> We stand in a coup when we've something to get,
> And here sounds like there after tea.
> For we're Norfolk and good, and we do different too;
> Abroad's what we sail on, but what's that to you?
> (*Do Different*)

20 October, Thursday

Returning from Knapton and the linguistic attentions of Mrs Mathews, we were forced to slow down behind a small boy and an even smaller animal. I was riding in the vicar's donkey cart, the only transport available, driven by Rev. Rudd. I asked the curate what sort of pathetic beast it was that was blocking our road. 'That is young Walter Kipper,' he replied.

I decided I might get more sense from the boy and it came to me that here was a chance to practice my new command of the local dialect. Stepping from the cart I approached the brat with care. I have translated the ensuing conversation into English: 'Tell me lad, what is that puny creature you lead?' I enquired. His reply was typical of the surly nature of the peasantry of these parts: 'What's it got to do with you?' he said. I was not to be put off so easily. 'Come lad,' I persisted. 'I will give you sixpence if you will tell me about it.'

This offer had the desired effect. He at once told me all about the animal, where it came from and where it was going. He told me that this pathetic creature, barely six hands high, was a ram and that he had fetched it from somewhere called Rollesby to take to the ship – a ship, it should be remembered, being a sheep. Or, of course, a ship. He assured me that in Rollesby this ram was considered far from small, being too large for their requirements and that he had therefore been able to get it cheaply. He concluded that when the ram reached St Just-near-Trunch it would be 'put to the ship'.

This puzzled me. Assuming that he meant sheep, and not ship, was I to believe that the sheep would be asked their opinion of the ram? How would it be put to them? How would they demonstrate their approval or otherwise? It all smacks too much of women's suffrage to me.

The lad, it seemed, had told me all he knew, which was little enough, and started to leave. It was with some difficulty that I persuaded him to give me threepence change.

****

To Sid Kipper this was yet more proof of Mrs Prewd's 'towniness':

> I thought everyone knew about putting the ram to the sheep. All it means is – well, everyone knows what it means. Otherwise where do they think little lambs come from? The point is that the ram knows his own business and all you have to do is put him with the sheep, and he'll get on with it. 'You don't keep a dog and bark yourself,' as they say, although Cyril Cockle used to!
>
> The Rollesby rams were special. You see, the people in Rollesby had a thing about breeding very small rams. Over the years they bred them smaller and smaller, and smaller. Of course, the breed's vanished now. Well, the rams couldn't reach up to the ewes no more.

21 October, Friday

Today is celebrated throughout the land as Trafalgar Day. Throughout the land, that is, except for this one pathetic little corner of it. I am no longer surprised by their lack of patriotism, but I am still disgusted by it. Next year will mark the centenary of Horatio Nelson's heroic death, but for all the effect his example has had here he need not have bothered. Thankfully, I shall be back in London by then and I have decided to join him in St Paul's to celebrate his early departure from this earth.

****

Horatio Nelson is often thought of as Norfolk's favourite son. Born at Burnham Thorpe, on the north Norfolk coast and educated at a number of Norfolk schools, he joined the navy at the age of twelve and the rest, as they say, is history. But I have uncovered a piece of that history which is not referred to in any of the reference books I've consulted. It seems that in 1799 Nelson came to Trunch as a guest of the Silver-Darlings. The old visitors book at the Hall has the following entry:

7th March — Mr and Mrs H. Smith: Arrived: drunk
                                     Left: with fleas in ears.

I have every reason to believe that this was Nelson and Lady Hamilton, travelling incognito, especially since we find the additional comment: 'This chap doesn't seem to be quite all there.'

Sid: Old Hori Nelson, he weren't too popular round these parts from the start. He kept on interfering with the smuggling, you see. The year before he visited here he had the Battle of the Nile, where he sunk a lot of French boats what was picking up a cargo for us. 'Course, he didn't know that's what they was doing, but he ought to have minded his own business. So when he come around here, boasting all about what he was and wasn't going to do to the French, that didn't go down too well. In the end someone give him a sock in the eye, but that didn't have a lot of effect 'cos he hadn't got that particular eye anyhow. I suppose it was more of a sock in the socket really.

26 October, Wednesday

I do believe I am beginning to make a maid of Maud. One might say that it is simply a matter of getting her to forget the 'I' and concentrate on the 'U'.

But enough of this word play. This morning she finally did everything right. She laid out the right clothes without being struck. She boiled my egg exactly as I like it. She even remembered not to blow her nose on her apron. My training is paying off. She really ought to pay me two shillings a week, rather than the other way around.

Of course, Maud would never do in London, for she still has far too much spirit in her. Here, in these murky backwaters, that does not matter. In fact it is almost an advantage, since she has no senior staff to lead her and I almost respect her for it. She is not unattractive, in an obvious sort of a way, and will one day make a good wife for some minor tradesman, perhaps, thus securing her future. If she does it will be no little thanks to my discipline and may lift her above the level of her family, who are situated socially some distance below the Plimsoll Line.

Wednesday is usually a quiet day in the village. Consequently I rarely require any particular duties from Maud, other than the routine ones of cooking, cleaning, fetching the coal, stoking the boiler, dusting, polishing the silver, painting the white stones along the front path, and so on. This afternoon was a case in point and I gave her an hour off to do with as she wished. She disappointed me by going to her room to lie down. There is still far too much indolence in her, I am afraid.

****

Maud Kipper never did marry her 'minor tradesman'. In 1906 she secured her own future by setting up in business for herself. The Maud Kipper School Of Maiding was a great success up until the First World War and employers would send girls to learn the basics of service. The course was straightforward, but thorough. It covered not only Cooking, Scrubbing and Skivvying, but also Admirers, Perks and Putting Your Feet Up And Having A Cuppa. So Maud did, in fact, benefit from her experience with Mrs Prewd.

30 October, Sunday

As I led Maud on her weekly walk this afternoon the stupid girl kept stopping to pick things up. By the end she had a bag full of something and on our return I demanded to know what it was. Imagine my disgust when she tipped out a mass of vegetation on to the table. Sweeping it all away with my stick and catching her smartly with the follow through, I asked what she meant by bringing such things into my house.

'I didn't mean nothing,' she protested. 'Of course you did not mean nothing,' I said. 'So just what was the something which you did mean?' I was rather proud of this rejoinder, but it went over Maud's head. She puzzled over it for some time, eventually muttering: 'I'm not sure what you mean by what did I mean.'

The conversation was heading towards a discussion of the meaning of meaning and I was sure that Maud had nothing to contribute to such a debate. I decided to try the monosyllabic approach. 'Why have you got all this stuff?' I asked. Her face cleared at once. 'Oh that! That's for the divining.' Now it was my turn to be puzzled, but I did not show it, preferring to settle for a moral victory. 'Why did you not say so at once?' I said and set her about her duties.

I wonder what this divining is? It seems to me that all matters divine come under the auspices of the vicar, so I will ask Rev. Mullett about it tomorrow.

****

Nowadays the form of divining we are most familiar with is water divining or dowsing. In days gone by, however, all sorts of divination were practised. The most common uses were by young men and women who wished to know who they would marry. Certain nights were considered especially good for this and Halloween was the best.

The forms of divination were legion. They involved apples, laurel leaves, eggs, onions, ivy, rosemary and no doubt parsley, sage and thyme as well. Unmarried readers who wish to make use of such methods should read *Know The Game – Divining*, by Miss Fuchsia Shock, from which this extract comes:

> Various forms of divination can indicate the actual identity of a future spouse. Leave some snails in a tin on All Hallows Eve, and in the morning they will have spelt out his or her initials. So will an

apple. Not, of course, if left in a tin overnight. You must take the skin off in one go, and then throw the peel over your shoulder.

Another favourite method is to induce dreams, in which the future partner will be seen. An onion, put under the pillow, is said to be effective – if rather lumpy.

It was only natural, then, that Maud would be collecting materials for divination. No doubt she was looking for the initials D. Q. F. S-D. I hope she used a large apple!

31 October, Monday

Rev. Mullett was most forthcoming this afternoon on the subject of divining. It is a means of finding out who one will marry. When he had explained it to me at some length I sympathised with him. It must be hard, I suggested, working among people with such primitive beliefs. Did he not find it offensive to his Christian principles?

'Oh no,' he said. 'I use it myself to find out the names of fallen women I can visit. It is but another aspect of God's mysterious nature.' This rather shocked me. I had not been aware that God had a mysterious nature. I had always assumed that God was strictly Church of England. 'Surely the practice is a heathen one,' I protested. 'Mrs Prewd,' he replied, quite unabashed, 'have you never considered the similarity of the words "heathen" and "heaven"?' I replied, pointedly, that there is a similar similarity between the words 'bullet' and 'bucket', but I could not see any significance in it.

I pondered the matter further as I returned home. It seems to me that if it is appropriate for a member of the Anglican clergy to use such methods, then so may I. I shall sleep tonight with an onion under my pillow, and if I should dream of Doyley Silver-Darling, then so be it.

****

Hallowtide marked the end of one half of the year in the old Icenic calendar, the other half being marked by May Day. On 31 October the beasts were brought in from the fields to be housed for the winter and magic was believed to be abroad.

'Shepherds' Delight' was the name given to November the first since they no longer had to spend their nights in the open with their flocks. With

116

the stock safely locked away they could make up for lost opportunities in The Goat Inn. This was known locally as 'barrelling' – hence the expression 'lock stock and barrel'.

NOVEMBER 1904

1 November, Tuesday

What a dreadful night I had. I shall never again try such a thing. I think I can now say with confidence that to divine is to err.

Perhaps you have never tried to sleep with an onion under your pillow. My previous acquaintance with the onion has been in its braised state, when it is soft and tender. The raw vegetable is an entirely different proposition: it is extremely hard and surprisingly knobbly. It took some time to push it down into the horse hair sufficiently to stop my head rolling off. Then I composed myself for sleep.

Sleep, however, was slow to come. My mind kept going back to the vicar's strange statement about the similarity of the words 'heaven' and 'heathen'. I thought of examples of similar words with quite different meanings. Bacon and Baron. Docker and Doctor. Peasant, and pleasant. I had just about decided that Rev. Mullett was wrong, and that I should get rid of the onion and forget the whole idea, when I fell asleep. Would that I had followed my own advice.

What I had was not a dream, but a nightmare. Instead of seeing Doyley Silver-Darling arrive to carry me off on a white charger I saw, in my sleep, a moth-eaten old cart-horse come trundling up the lane. Astride it, with a leg either side and another sticking up in front of him, was Maud's abominable brother, Albert.

This, however, was not the worst of it. One might expect to meet Albert Kipper in a nightmare – that is where he belongs. What made the whole thing quite unbearable was that in my dream I came running out of the house, dressed in white muslin, sprang joyfully onto the horse behind him and rode off with him into the sunset. At this point I woke up in floods of tears caused, to some extent, by the onion, which had burst beneath my pillow. After that I was afraid to go to sleep again and spent the night in an armchair.

****

In country areas there were experts in explaining the meaning of dreams. In St Just anyone with a dream which needed interpretation went to Mundesley, to see Old Mother Shipham.

Old Mother Shipham had more than one approach to the dreams of her customers. For instance, when Cyril Cockle had a dream in which he met seven fat cows followed by seven thin ones she told him that he would meet fourteen cows, of various sizes. But when Farmer Trout had exactly the same dream she gave him a full written report:

> The first fat cow represents the fatted calf, grown old through waiting for the prodigal son to return. The second fat cow is The Dun Cow public house at Salthouse. The third fat cow is Trunch Football Club, as shown by its initials. The fourth fat cow is the Great Cow of Calthorpe, symbol of peace and plenty. The fifth fat cow is the Cow With The Crumpled Horn, which represents your manhood. The sixth fat cow is the cow which jumped over the moon, which will, of course, give green cheese. The seventh fat cow is Lady Silver-Darling. The thin cows are spares.
>
> The meaning of the dream is clear. You will have a sexual encounter with Lady Silver-Darling and the Trunch Football Club somewhere between Salthouse and Calthorpe – perhaps at Baconsthorpe. There will be peace, due to the non-return of the prodigal son, and plenty of green cheese.

You may wonder why Farmer Trout got such a complete analysis, while Cyril Cockle had only the simplest of explanations. The answer, of course, is that the Farmer went privately, while Cyril was a charity case.

3 November, Thursday

This afternoon I was waiting at my gate for Rev. Rudd, who was late to take me to Knapton, when Farmer Trout came up the lane on his wagon. He slowed down and asked if he could give me a lift. 'Not unless you are going to Knapton,' I replied. 'Oh no,' he frowned. 'I never go there. Funny lot they are. That comes of them being foreign.'

By now he had come to a halt alongside me so, just to be polite, I asked where he was going. 'To my farm,' he said. 'Today is a very important day for me. You wouldn't be interested, but I'm hoping to have a good thrashing in my barn.'

It seemed to me that Farmer Trout was getting ideas above his station. Such things as a good thrashing are more suited to members of the House of Lords. I wondered whether he might not forget such elevated notions if I were the one to apply the blows. I have trained myself to be slow to show mercy.

With this in mind I said 'Perhaps I could come along and help with your thrashing, Farmer Trout.' He appeared rather surprised.

Scratching his chin he answered slowly. 'Well, you're hardly dressed for it, but you can come along if you want. Here, jump up on the cart.' I was so excited at the prospect of teaching Farmer Trout a lesson he could not forget that I forgot all about Rev. Rudd and my appointment with Mrs Mathews.

When we got to the barn I found a number of Farmer Trout's so-called labourers already there, standing about with jointed bits of wood in their hands. Here, I thought, was one local custom of which I might heartily approve. I was given my own cudgel and invited to take off my coat. I did so with relish.

'Now, Mrs Pratt,' began the farmer, at which I made a mental note that this time he would pay for refusing to remember my name, 'as you are our guest you shall have the honour of the first blows. Shall we say a hundred to start with?' Clearly the man was showing off. A hundred blows would surely kill him. Nevertheless, I agreed at once: it guaranteed me the pleasure of having him beg me to stop.

Now it was my turn to be surprised. How was I to know that thrashing is an agricultural operation? Not just any agricultural operation, but a dirty, dusty, arduous one, fit only for those born to it. I could not complain, however, without admitting my previous ignorance. So I had to flail away till dark, those first hundred blows followed by hundreds more, until I was finally able to crawl home to a mineral bath, which did little to ease my poor stiff back.

****

Thrashing, or threshing, was a winter job which could be done indoors. It was back-breaking work, for the flail was heavy and it had to be kept moving in rhythm with others. The introduction of the threshing machine certainly saved any number of aching backs. Nowadays, of course, the grain is removed from the ears by the combine harvester all in one go. Away Farm must have been one of the last in the county to thresh by hand.

Sid: Old Trout had a thing about the thrashing. Originally he insisted that the thrashing had to be done by hand. Eventually, of course, he had to give in to modern ways and let them use flails like everyone else. But he wouldn't have no machine thrashed grain on his farm. He said they'd thrash by machine at Away Farm over his dead body. Which is why they buried him in the Great Barn.

> This land is my land, so you keep off it,
> I sow the crops here and reap the profit.
> From that big oak tree to the Parish Bound'ry
> This land belongs to me alone.
> (*This is my Land*)

5 November, Saturday

All day long people have been collecting up old dead trees and placing them neatly in piles. As I passed through the village I noticed these piles with approval, feeling that they would stand to remind people of how much pleasanter the area would be if it were always kept tidy in this manner.

Sadly, however, this was not to be. No sooner had darkness fallen than they were all set alight. I only hope that the arsonist is caught before he has a chance to do any further damage.

****

In St Just, November the fifth is known as Burns Night, after the eighteenth-century character 'Rabbit' Burns. It's not clear how Burns got his nickname, but many of the villagers still claim to carry his blood, if not his name – he never married.

To mark the occasion, bonfires were lit and a great supper held, at which the various parcels of common land – or plots – were redistributed for the next year. In the nineteenth century, this distribution was often bitterly fought over. Gunfire was not unknown and many alliances were formed and broken – hence the association of the date with 'gunpowder, treason and plots'.

More recently the business has been organised by the Parish Council and it has become a peaceful event, whose chief feature is a sheep's stomach, filled with oats and offal, which is ceremonially piped in, to the accompaniment of the Trunch blowpipes. Then, so as not to put people off their supper, it is ceremonially piped out again.

6 November, Sunday

I had asked Miss Pickerel to tea in order to put her in her place, following the incident at the tea rooms last month. Due to the sparsity of halfway decent people around here I cannot afford to cut her completely, but she must be reminded that only a few months ago I had to rescue her from underneath a heap of revolting school-girls.

I think the fact that all the chairs except my own had been removed, forcing her to sit on a little stool at my feet, gave her the right idea. To reinforce this, when Maud asked if she should pour the tea I said 'Oh no, Miss Pickerel can do that.' When she had poured the tea, toasted the muffins, passed the cakes and cleared the table, I think she was beginning to get the point.

After she had gone, thanking me fulsomely for allowing her to leave, I had a warm feeling that at least one thing was right in the world. I am sure that she will be much happier in the place God and I have given her.

11 November, Friday

I have spent the whole of today with a feeling that there is something I should have remembered, but for the life of me I cannot think what it is. I did not forget to attend my last elocution lesson yesterday, and I have certainly not forgotten the that I have only a further four months and thirteen days to suffer here. No matter: whatever it is I will remember it eventually.

There were extra services in church, for this is St Just's Day. The vicar enjoined us never to forget St Just's life and works, and to keep them in mind as a source of inspiration for the rest of the year. I am sure these are admirable sentiments, but as he told us nothing about said life and works it may prove difficult. I asked Rev. Mullett to tell me about St Just, but he seemed unwilling, other than to inform me that she led a life of great personal privation and poverty. I fail to see how that can be of any interest to me.

What did interest me was the appearance of Doyley Silver-Darling in church. It is the first time I have seen him since he was unable to keep our assignation of a month ago. I asked him if his headache was gone and was sorry when he told me it had just

123

returned, that very moment. Visibly forcing a smile, despite the pain, he asked after my own health. I replied that I am well and asked if I might call on him at the Hall. 'I cannot, at the moment, think why not,' he replied, so I suggested a time which would conveniently fit in with an invitation to dinner. This was not immediately forthcoming, but there is still time before Monday.

****

St Just is not one of our better known saints. She did not slay any dragons. She failed to drive out any snakes. She did once, according to legend, squash a snail, but that was probably an accident. But who was she?

The question has exercised scholars for centuries. Dr Graham Perch, who has dedicated his life to the study of St Just, says this is just one example of her benign influence: 'Most scholars could do with the exercise', he explains in his book *The Insteps of St Just* :

> St Just was not, as some have suggested, Justus of Canterbury, the Archbishop who fled to Gaul and died in 627 A.D. There is no evidence, in fact, that a woman has ever been Archbishop of Canterbury.
>
> There are many legends surrounding the holy woman of Norfolk. In one story she meets, in the middle of nowhere, a man with a withered leg, who can walk only with the aid of a stick. She takes the stick from him, plants it in the ground and it miraculously sprouts and grows into a 30-foot tree before his very eyes. Typically, she refuses his thanks and leaves him clutching the tree in gratitude. In another story she is seated in her cave when a stranger comes to her. 'I am a stranger to these parts,' he says, 'having just come from London. I am being pursued by local ruffians. Will you save me holy woman?' She rises from the ground, goes to the entrance of the cave, and calls to the ruffians. 'What is the meaning of this?' she asks them and their leader replies: 'This man has come here and because he has money he wants the best house and the best cows, and to come and go as he wants.' St Just ponders, then says to the leader: 'Take him away and do with him what you will – we can do without his sort around here.'
> (Chapter 1 – Just Put It There)

It is stories like this that keep St Just's memory alive in the village which bears her name.

14 November, Monday

Today I prepared for my meeting with Doyley Silver-Darling. Duly bathed, perfumed, brushed and dressed I arrived at the Great Hall in good time. I had not received a dinner invitation, but still had every hope of being asked to stay.

His Lordship's butler showed me to Doyley's rooms, where Herring announced me. I do not consider 'It's that woman, sir' to be a proper or sufficient introduction, and if Herring were my man I would make a point of clipping his fins. All this, however, was forgotten when I saw Doyley. He was dressed casually, in dressing gown and slippers, but rose to meet me, shook my hand and offered me a seat.

I started, as one does, to discuss the weather, but Doyley waved this away. 'It will soon be time for dinner,' he said. 'Perhaps we should come to the point.' I agreed whole-heartedly. He looked at me. I looked at him. He looked puzzled. 'Well then,' he said. 'What is it?' 'What is what?' I replied, now puzzled myself. 'Mrs Prewd, you asked to call on me and here you are, so what do you want?'

He had me at a disadvantage. I had simply wanted to see him, in the hope that something might, well, happen. Uncle Wesley came to my rescue. He always said: 'Put your cards on the table, but keep a few aces up your sleeve.' 'I simply wanted to see if you were alright,' I said, blushing a little. 'Well then,' Doyley replied masterfully, 'you've seen me now, alright, so you can go home happy. I'm going to dress for dinner. Goodbye.'

Looking back I do not think I can count the visit a success.

15 November, Tuesday

First thing this morning Herring returned my muff, which was most infuriating. I had quite deliberately left it at the Great Hall yesterday in order that I might have an excuse to call and recover it. I had hoped I might meet Doyley again. The fact that Herring is unaware that this is what a lady does under such circumstances does not surprise me, however. There is something about that man which makes him quite unfit to serve such as Doyley. I had to speak to him myself for his surliness. I told him that I hoped he would one day get his just deserts from his master. His enigmatic reply was that he shared my hopes.

125

After Herring had left I spent some time trying to devise a way to meet Doyley more often, but as yet I have not hit upon quite the right thing. No doubt something will come to me in time.

16 November, Wednesday

After some thought I have had an idea that should bring Doyley and I together more. If I invited him to be Honorary President of some sort of worthy association, I thought, he could scarcely refuse. I would be a prominent member of said association, of course. Thinking along these lines I have decided to start the Trunch Musical Appreciation Society. Such a thing is sorely needed here in any case.

We must be clear just what sort of music it is that we will appreciate. Certainly not the rough, rude music of the peasantry. Nor the vulgar music of the dance hall. Nor again the horrid modern music of the likes of Mr Ben Jarmine-Brighton. The sort of music that we will appreciate will be the music of the drawing room and the concert hall. The sort of music which may only be heard properly in evening dress, having paid for one's tickets in guineas.

I have written to Doyley asking him to be our President and implying that this was what I wished to ask him on Monday. He may think that it simply slipped my mind. Now I must begin a membership drive. It will not be easy to find the right sort of person, but I console myself with the thought that the smaller our numbers the more intimate our acquaintance.

****

St Just-near-Trunch was full of music. There was the church, where a hand-pumped organ led the faithful in hymns and Psalms. There was the chapel, known for its lusty singing. There was music and singing at The Goat Inn, in people's houses, even in the streets at certain times. The village even had its own much prized band, the Trunch Coronation Band, although it had ceased to function by Mrs Prewd's time.

Sid: The most musical people in St Just have always been the Kipper family. Which is how I've now become a famous star, travelling up and down the land singing all the old songs from Trunch and telling people all about them. I don't mean posh songs what hardly

126

anyone can understand. I mean what they call folk-songs – which no one can understand.

As a matter of fact, I've even been researching some new old songs! I found one recently, which is an old protest song about saving the dodo. Of course, it hadn't been sung for a while, because it's a bit pointless now, but I reckon that's what old folk songs are all about.

Anyhow, what I'm saying is, when it comes to musical apprehension in St Just then it's the people who come and listen to me you ought to talk to.

How many roads must a dodo walk down
Before you can call her a dodo?
How many seas must a white dodo sail
Before she can sleep in the road-oh?
Ripe fruits and berries and nuts that are nigh,
In the bird's stomach are stowed-oh;
Be grateful good people the dodo don't fly,
For t'would danger when she unload-oh.
And if you should question on what she had dined
The answer my friend would be blowing in the wynde.

(*The Innocent Dodo*)

---

19 November, Saturday

Today saw the first meeting of the Trunch Musical Appreciation Society. We were a small, but select, group. Doyley Silver-Darling could not attend, having been called away to London at short notice, but he has agreed to be our Honorary President.

Assembled in my drawing room were Miss Pickerel, Rev. Mullett, Lady Silver-Darling and myself. We were joined by Mr and Mrs Babcock, from nearby Bradfield. Mr Babcock – or Reginald as he insists we call him – is a self-made man, although I suggest he would have turned out better with some assistance! Still, he was educated at Eton, he told us, and went to Cambridge. His wife, Edith, is rather common. Men, of course, are such fools in these matters. But she was pleasant enough, if a little out of her depth.

Our meeting went well, lacking just one thing for the completest achievement of its aims. It would have been nice to have some music to appreciate. Miss Pickerel felt that her talents on the violoncello were inadequate to the purpose and we declined Mr Babcock's offer to hum a selection from the Brandenburg Concertos on the grounds that we should honour the composer's wishes with regard to instrumentation. Nevertheless we have made an encouraging start.

Our next meeting will be at the Great Hall, where Her Ladyship has kindly consented to put her son's gramophone at our disposal. I only hope that Doyley himself will be there to operate it.

****

Reginald Babcock was an impostor. That is he was who he said he was, but not quite what he said he was. For example, he didn't go to the school we normally think of as Eton. He actually went to the City of Norwich School in Eaton, Norwich. And while he did once go to Cambridge, it was only to visit an elderly aunt.

He made his money in ladies' underwear. During the Victorian era it was extremely difficult to trade in such items, since, as a matter of decency, they could never be mentioned. For instance, a salesman visiting the manager of a shop couldn't actually tell him what he was selling, let alone show him. And nobody could go into a shop and actually ask for an item of underwear. So unless the assistant could guess what the customer wanted, it's hard to see how Victorian women acquired these intimate items at all. Some were forced to steal them, that being a lesser evil than actually mentioning them openly. Which is where Mr Babcock came in.

As a lift boy in a large store in Norwich he realised that if a lady going into the shop couldn't say what she wanted, then she couldn't say she didn't want it, either. He took over the lease of the store and, by means of sign language, instructed all the assistants that they were to supply every account holder with an item of ladies' underwear, once a month. The customer could not complain without describing the item, which they could not do. Indeed, the male customers could not even admit to knowing what the items were. They were forced, then, to pay their accounts without comment. In ten years, from 1887 to 1897 he sold more underwear from his one shop than was supplied to the entire city of London. Norwich became famous for its consumption of underwear.

The arrival of Edward VII on the throne in 1901 brought sweeping changes and before long people were talking about little else but ladies' underwear. But by then Mr Babcock, or Sir Reginald as he was to become, had retired to his estate in Bradfield with Edith, his wife and former store detective.

128

21 November, Monday

This evening saw a succession of callers, all asking to see 'the man of the house'. By the fourth such episode I had become thoroughly fed up with hearing Maud's explanations to them. Answering the door myself I grasped the man concerned firmly by his ear, into which I spoke loudly and clearly. 'Before you ask to see the man of the house you will tell me why you wish to see him.' I did not consider 'Get off missus' an adequate reply, so I grasped his other ear in my other hand and repeated the request. After a certain amount of twisting I managed to elicit the fact that he was canvassing for election to the Parish Council. He left looking like the second of the three wise monkeys.

My next caller was a woman. 'Surely you cannot be standing for the Parish Council?' I asked her. 'Oh no. I'm asking your support for our Votes for Women campaign,' she replied. After half an hour or so I think she was quite aware of my views on that particular matter. I doubt they coincide with hers one little bit.

It is difficult to imagine why these women should want the vote. If men wish to fool themselves that they can have some influence then so be it. I have every faith that Lady Silver-Darling will continue to be the power behind the throne in this area.

✳✳✳✳✳✳✳✳✳✳

Parish Council elections in St Just-near-Trunch were keenly contested. After years of near feudalism the ordinary people of the village were delighted to have a say in the way things were run, even if that say went largely unheard by Lord Silver-Darling.

Membership of the council brought with it certain advantages. There were the late night meetings in The Goat. Then there were trips to other parishes to see how things were done there. And, of course, there were the footpaths.

Footpaths nowadays are used mainly for recreation, but in the past they were the arteries of village life. They had certain distinct advantages over made-up roads and lanes. Constable Crabb could not pursue you along them on his bicycle, for instance. Nor could Lord Silver-Darling ride his carriage along them and horsewhip you through the window. And they led to some very interesting places. Woods that contained game. The rear entrance of The Goat Inn. Not to mention the back door of Widow Hake's bungalow. They were the secret channels of the working classes and as such the Parish Council guarded them jealously.

Lord Silver-Darling hated footpaths. He never used them himself, and resented the fact that many of them passed over his land. One of his chief amusements was releasing bulls into fields through which footpaths passed. He would have his coach drawn up at a suitable vantage point and laugh himself hoarse as he watched the poor villagers being forced to jump over hedges, dive into ditches, vault gates or swarm up trees. This hobby of his had an unexpected side effect at the Stockholm Olympics of 1912, where Maureen Moray won a gold medal in the Old Fashioned Pentathlon. Years of dodging bulls on footpaths had honed her to perfection in the five events – high jump, diving, vaulting, climbing and bullfighting.

27 November, Sunday

Today, as Rev. Mullett reminded us in church, is Advent Sunday. We begin four weeks of preparation for the second greatest festival in the Christian calendar. I do hope it will be celebrated in a suitably simple manner. At least there should be none of the crass commercialism here which is creeping into the season in London. Most people here are much too poor to indulge in commercialism, although the crassness would come to them naturally.

As I left the church an old man stood at the door with his hat held out. 'Christmas is coming,' he told me, as if I might not be aware of the fact. I ignored him. 'The goose is getting fat,' he went on. I continued to ignore him. 'Please put a penny in the old man's hat,' he persisted. Still getting no response he went on 'If you haven't got a penny, then a halfpenny will do.' I decided that he must be too ignorant to appreciate being ignored. 'An overweight goose is best put on a reducing diet and given regular exercise,' I told him. 'I suggest you stop loitering here, bothering honest folk, and take it for a good long walk.' He looked undecided, so I helped him make up what he uses in place of a mind by propelling him along with my boot. It is so satisfying to be able to help the poor in such ways. I shall count it my first act of goodwill to all men.

****

Mrs Prewd was to be disappointed in her wish for a simple Christmas. In north-east Norfolk Christmas was celebrated as a festival second to none. In those days there were no Summer holidays, no Spring breaks, no long weekends. Christmas was the big one.

Sid: Of course, years ago Christmas didn't start nearly as soon as it does now. We never used to have the season of Advert going on for months and months. Strictly speaking Christmas didn't begin until Christmas Eve – which was still a day early, really. Then they had the twelve days of Christmas, which went on until January 6th – although if you include Christmas Eve then it was really thirteen days, so it was a sort of bakers' twelve days. So the idea was to get all the religious stuff out of the way early on so they could enjoy Christmas properly.

<u>DECEMBER 1904</u>

On the first day of Xmas, my dog
and I brought back:

A partridge in an old sack,

2 more hens,

3 lame ducks,

4 bald coots,

5 poached eggs,

6 bootiful turkeys,

7 pleasant pheasants,

8 stoned crows,

9 breeding rabbits,

10 hares receding,

11 salmon smoking,

12 stags a rutting.

(*The Poacher's Christmas*)

3 December, Saturday

The Trunch Musical Appreciation Society met this evening at the Great Hall, as guests of the Silver-Darlings. Sadly Doyley was not present, being kept up in Town, but he sent his father to take his place.

After the formalities I suggested it was time to listen to some music. 'I hope you're not going to sing,' said His Lordship. I explained that we had come to the Hall to avail ourselves of the gramophone and asked whether he would be good enough to operate the machine for us. 'No idea how the damned thing works,' was his reply. 'Send for Herring, or whatever his name is.'

What Herring was doing at the Hall when his master was in London I do not know. He was called, however, and instructed to operate the gramophone. Before long we were being subjected to a selection of excerpts from H.M.S. Pinafore.

I demanded to know what he meant by playing such rubbish. 'That's all the music there is,' he replied. 'It's what the young master likes.' His Lordship opined that he thought it was 'Damned jolly. Better than all that high falutin' stuff you get at the Albert Hall.'

We had no choice but to abandon the gramophone and spend the rest of the evening listening to Cynthia Silver-Darling play the piano. She claimed the pieces were by Mozart. Some of the pieces may indeed have been by Mozart, but they had been stuck together in a form even he would have failed to recognise.

It was not a successful meeting.

****

What was Herring doing in St Just-near-Trunch when his master was in London? In *I Did It* we find the answer. Or rather, we find that we've asked the wrong question.

At one time they had a society of some of the people my master most disliked. He called them the Trunch Mutual Appreciation Society. He was obliged to become their Honorary President, but swore that He would never go to any meetings.

Hardly had He so sworn than we arrived up from Town to find an invitation to one of their meetings the very next day. Worse still, the meeting was to be held at the Hall, using His private gramophone.

As I served dinner the night before – their butler having been given the evening off – I heard my master tell Her Ladyship that He would on no account attend the meeting. 'But who will operate the machine?' she asked. 'Herring can do it,' He replied and I cursed Him profusely under my breath for volunteering me to work on my own night off.

Her Ladyship reluctantly agreed to say that He was up in London. So my master spent the evening in The Goat Inn, while I wore out my arm winding that accursed machine. This led to a severe bout of butler's elbow and I was quite unable to beat the junior staff for several days.

(Chapter 15 – In My Lady's Chamber)

The T. M. A. S. never had to run the gauntlet of the Silver-Darlings again. Mr Babcock was so impressed with the gramophone that he sent to Norwich for one at once, along with a selection of classical records. After that, meetings were held at his house. But the Honorary President never attended.

4 December, Sunday

In church this morning I realised that my wish for a quiet Christmas season has so far been granted. There has been none of the hullaba-loo one would expect by now in London. Indeed, apart from a small notice in the corner shop announcing 'An Evening of Seasonal Readings and Sausage Rolls with the Vicar', today's service was the first reminder of Christmas I have had for a week.

The lessons were new to me, although a certain section about the beasts of the fields certainly rang true. I could see some of them in the aisle opposite, with mud on the soles of their unpolished boots. After the service I mentioned my unfamiliarity with the liturgy to Rev. Mullett, but he simply said that I was bound to find it strange, being a stranger. How odd. I hardly think of myself as a stranger here anymore.

The man with the overweight goose was outside the church again, but when he saw me coming he put his hat on and ran off. I can only assume he was reminded to take it for it's walk. Looking back I saw Farmer Trout pushing through the crowd in my direction, waving his hand and shouting that he wanted to 'have a word' with me. Having no wish to hear any words that man might know and recalling a saying of Uncle Wesley's that 'desertion is the better part of valour', I made a hasty retreat to the Old Toll House.

As the vicar might say: 'being a commoner I find Trout very common'.

****

During Advent it was traditional in St Just's to abandon the usual services and use the Book of Uncommon Prayer. This contains many rarities, such as the Call Collect, the Withouter Prayer and readings from St Just's Letters to the Friesians. These contain some fine passages, though why St Just chose to address her thoughts to a herd of cows is not clear.

5 December, Monday

I suppose I should have expected that Farmer Trout would not be easily put off. Today he succeeded in having his threatened word of yesterday. Indeed, he had several words, each of which I understood, though the sum of them meant nothing to me at all.

It was after luncheon that a knock came at the door. Maud answered it and I heard Trout rudely declare 'I can show myself in.' This he proceeded to do, catching me with the top button of my blouse undone. I hastily threw my hands up to my throat and held them there to cover my embarrassment. Before I could demand an apology and ask his business he had begun to conduct it.

'I expect it'll be an oversight,' he began, 'but you being, in a manner of speaking, the overseer, I'm here to ask you to look into it. If it's good enough for schoolmarms then I'm sure it's good enough for farmers and I dare say I'd appreciate the appreciation as much as the next man. And what I'm saying is, the next man should be me.'

He was speaking with such vehemence that I clasped my hands together in a sort of defensive reflex. Given their position this choked off any reply I might have made. Thankfully he seemed to be coming to his conclusion more rapidly than has proved the case on previous visits.

'My society is quite good enough for your society, if I'm any judge – which I am, at the North Walsham pig show every year. So now I've raised the matter I'll let you sleep on it. I expect you'll do the decent thing and I'll hear from you presently.'

By now I was beginning to feel faint from the effect of my hands gripping my windpipe, so I began to stand. It was my intention to rush into the kitchen, where I could fasten my button, regain my composure, and then return to tell the oaf what I thought of his judgement. He misinterpreted my movement, however. 'Don't bother to get up,' he said. 'I can show myself out.' Which he did.

Whether I gasped the more for lack of air or for that man's sheer effrontery I do not know, but it was some time before I recovered my composure. I am now, thankfully, quite restored, but I still have no idea what he was talking about. I only hope he feels the better for airing the matter, whatever it was.

****

Sid: Old Trout was an expert on saddlefront pigs. They reckon he could have been a national judge if he hadn't been the only person who bred them.

He was a big man in the village and he liked people to know it. Which they did. So that was alright. But if he thought he was being left out of something he used to get proper upset. I remember when he was left off the list of 'possibles' for the St Just football team. He busted into the next selection meeting and demanded they put him on the list. 'I've always been a possible,' he said, 'and I shall stand here and make myself impossible till you make me a possible again.' That was when he was 83.

Mind you, I am a bit biased. You see, Trout once gave my old father a special award at North Walsham – Biggest Pig at the Show – which just shows you what a good judge he was.

6 December, Tuesday

This morning Maud woke me at an early hour, clearly agitated. 'Have you slept on it?' she asked. Only half awake and assuming that for some peculiar reason she thought I might not have slept on my bed, I muttered that I had. I added that I was, in fact, still trying to do so. 'Good,' she replied, ignoring my implied reproach, 'because he'll want to know.' With that she left, threatening me with breakfast. Unable to regain sleep I rose and dressed. Then I went downstairs to demand from Maud an explanation of, and apology for, her extraordinary behaviour. When I had received the explanation, however, all thoughts of an apology fled my mind.

To sleep on something, Maud told me, is to consider it overnight. The matter I am supposed to have considered is Farmer Trout's demand to join the Trunch Musical Appreciation Society. Apparently he feels he has been slighted in the eyes of the village by not being invited to join us. The thought of that man delivering his opinions on music – no doubt from a standing position in the middle of the room – is simply preposterous. I would rather disband the Society.

8 December, Thursday

I have lost a great deal of sleep over the matter on which, ironically, I am supposed to have been sleeping. While I would rather die than share the Trunch Musical Appreciation Society with the likes of Farmer Trout, to disband it would be a betrayal of the very purpose for which the Society was founded. I refer, of course, to the purpose of bringing Doyley Silver-Darling and myself together. It is such a dilemma that yesterday I was driven to the desperate position of asking Miss Pickerel for her opinion – without, that is, revealing the exact nature of the problem.

Today, unable to quite find a superior solution which, given more time, I am sure I would arrive at, I have reluctantly decided to accept Miss Pickerel's suggestion. As it is imperative that Doyley and I continue to have a reason to meet we must, sadly, invite Farmer Trout to our next meeting and, as she put it, 'see how it goes'.

10 December, Saturday

Today I was once again surprised by Farmer Trout. On this occasion, however, I was also delighted. It happened in the late afternoon, when a knock at the door brought Maud in to say that there was someone called Stan with a message. As I went to the door I feared it might be one of those awful Methodists. Indeed he may well have been one – he looked the type. His message, however, was much more welcome here than any of their dangerous, subversive nonsense.

'Afternoon ma'am,' he said. 'Farmer Trout asked me to call round in my fourses to say he's got someone to read your letter and he's glad you've done the decent thing, and thank you very much and we'll say no more about it.'

At this point he raised his cap, as if to leave. Instead, however, he began to scratch his head, whilst screwing up his face in concentration.

'There's another bit,' he muttered. Then his face cleared to its previous, simple state. 'Oh yes. He say he have noted the date of the next meeting and he send his apologies for that and any other meetings you might have and don't even let him know when they are because he can't stand all that high fluting music and give him a good old polka on the squeezebox any day, and even better with a bit of step dancing.'

Clearly relieved to be rid of his burden he put his cap back on and tramped off up the lane to Away Farm, his 'fourses' flapping around his ankles.

This news has put me in high spirits. I had not imagined that such a satisfactory resolution could be achieved. There will be no Farmer Trout at our meetings and no reason to avoid him any longer – apart from the obvious one of taste. I am delighted that the matter is now effectively closed, and to celebrate I have allowed myself an extra glass of port and Maud an extra glass of water.

****

Mrs Prewd clearly didn't think much of Methodists. It's easy to see why, since at that time it was very much a church for the labouring classes. In many Norfolk villages they had to build their chapels on the outskirts, as landowners wouldn't give permission to build in the village.

The main reason why Methodists were hated by the establishment was their association with the trades unions. Val Marlin, in her book *Methodism in their Madness* , discusses the matter:

> In north-east Norfolk the battle between the farmers and the agricultural unions was especially bitter. USBAT – the Union of Swede Bashers and Allied Trades – had close connections with the Methodist Church and this was much resented by the farmers, who saw themselves as second only to the Anglican clergy in the chain of command from God to labourer. The fact that the Methodists selected lay preachers from their own ranks was especially worrying, as was the implied equality of their use of the term 'brother'.

Some of the larger farmers formed their own union, the F.U., and tried to forge connections with the Church Of England, who they saw as their natural allies. Initial negotiations went well, but they stuck on the matter of what they should call each other. 'Brother' already meant monk. 'Father' had other religious connections. Some favoured 'mate', but this would have been confusing in the fishing villages. The discussion went on and on. In the end it became so heated that it was unnecessary for them to find any form of address, as they were no longer talking to each other. (Chapter 6 – Close a Union)

Incidentally, I should point out that fourses is not an item of clothing related to plus fours. It is a break for food, just like elevenses – though at a different time, of course.

> Come all you bold young farmers, this message ne'er forget:
> Though you are strong, united we will be stronger yet.
> If we stand firm together we soon will have our way:
> Longer hours for lower wages, and shorter holidays.
> Join the Farmer's Union, join the favoured few,
> Let our cry go yonder – 'We are the great F.U.'
> (*Song Of The F.U.*)

13 December, Tuesday

Tomorrow I am to attend the vicar's evening of seasonal readings and sausage rolls. I am sure it will be intriguing, if only to solve the question of who Augustus Swineherd is.

Or should the question be who Augustus Swineherd are? That is to say, if the man giving some of the readings is to be Augustus Swineherd, then who was the Augustus Swineherd who apparently wrote prose and poetry throughout the eighteenth and nineteenth centuries? Or will we be treated to a dramatic impersonation of the man who wrote those works? If so, then who wrote the contemporary pieces which are advertised as coming from the same pen?

My companion for the evening will be Miss Pickerel. I could think of nobody more suitable or desirable. That is to say, I can think of a host of people both more suitable and more desirable than Miss Pickerel, but all of them, unfortunately, live in or near London. Had Doyley Silver-Darling been at the Hall I might have taken courage enough to invite him, but he too is in London.

I will say this for Miss Pickerel – she does now know her place. She has the decency to walk a pace behind me if we are out together and she has learned not to speak unless spoken to.

****

The Augustus Swineherd of Mrs Prewd's time was the fifth Trunch Laureate of the same name. This hereditary post was accidentally created by Lord Silver-Darling in 1784, when he granted the 72-year-old Augustus Swineherd a pension for life for his writing. Due to a carelessly drawn up contract his son, Augustus Swineherd, was then able to take up the pension. Since then, despite several court cases and various threats, the Silver-Darlings have been unable to free themselves of the index-linked contract. As long as the Augustus Swineherds continue to write they can claim the pension, plus bonus payments for readings, and so on.

The current Augustus Swineherd, under her various pen names, leads the modern literary life. She appears on television chat shows, hosts weekend writers' courses and attends book signings. Of course, she employs ghost writers to write the actual books.

14 December, Wednesday

Whilst tonight's readings varied in quality, the sausage rolls were without exception quite inedible to anyone with a decent palate. Needless to say they were eagerly consumed by the local populace.

Many of the readings were quite uplifting, although some were too modern for my taste. Others were dubious in their sentiments. In particular a piece called 'A Christmas with Carol' was almost calculated to spread dissent. It told the story of a rich man who is visited by three spirits and decides to give all of his money to the poor. I think we can well do without that sort of dangerous nonsense.

Unfortunately I was unable to solve the riddle of Augustus Swineherd. Indeed, I am now even more puzzled than before. Why did Lord Silver-Darling hand him a shilling after each reading? I did not like to ask anyone lest I appear ignorant.

140

On the whole the evening was pleasant enough. I would have liked to have been asked to contribute myself, but I expect the vicar thought the contrast would be unfair to the other readers. I shall go to sleep with the words of one of the pieces going through my mind:

> It was Christmas Eve in the workhouse;
> It was Christmas Eve in Peru;
> But in The Goat Inn it was bonfire night
> For all that anyone knew.

I wonder what it means?

****

The vicar's evening of Christmas readings is still very much a living tradition in St Just-near-Trunch.

Sid: Well, it's more half dead really. You just don't get the quality of reading nowadays. She was lucky she got to hear some proper readers. By all accounts old Mullett and Swineherd V could really give it some wally. We have to put up with the new vicar, Rev. 'Call Me Derek' Bream. And the sausage rolls got done away with years ago, 'cause some of the incomers made a fuss on account of they didn't eat meat. I don't know where they got the idea 'Porky' Pilchard puts any meat in his sausage rolls!

18 December, Sunday

I had been coming to terms with the strange liturgy Rev. Mullett has been using recently, but today's service was beyond the pale. One would not see the like in London. For instance, I have never before seen a minister of the Church of England take a service dressed as Father Christmas.

At least, that is how Rev. Mullett tells me he was dressed. It looked far from the jolly, red-coated and white-bearded Father Christmas that I know. Not, you understand, that I actually know any of them personally. The vicar wore tights, a brown, belted jerkin and a crown of greenery which kept slipping off his head and hanging from one or the other of his rather prominent ears.

He did this in order to take part in what he called a 'mummers

141

play'. He played the part of Old Nick, which I am given to understand is a diminutive of Saint Nicholas. The play involved much shouting, singing and sword-play, but its religious significance escaped me entirely. It culminated in Albert Kipper felling Saint George with his wooden leg, which I gather was not actually in the script and led to the play coming to a thankfully early conclusion.

Afterwards I tackled Rev. Mullett on the inclusion of such pagan buffoonery in an act of worship. He replied that in a rural area it is necessary to make some concessions to local ways or else no one will attend. 'If you cannot beat them, you must join them,' proclaimed the vicar, wiping his hands on his tights. Personally I would be delighted to take on the task of beating each and every one of them to within an inch of their worthless lives.

All this so distracted me that I forgot to ask him about Augustus Swineherd. Perhaps he wrote the mummers play as well.

****

Sid Kipper, who has taken part in recent revivals of the play, was incredulous at this last remark:

> Anyone could tell you that Swineherd didn't write the mummers play. No one wrote the mummers play, because it's traditional and things that are traditional aren't written by anyone. They just get handed down, like old clothes.
>
> All these old plays were looked after by a particular group of people, who used to perform them. In some places that was the Grocers' play or the Wheelwrights' play, and so on. Round our way it was the Night-soil Man's Play, which is why it died out, due to modern plumbing.

21 December, Wednesday

I have found out who Augustus Swineherd is. Or rather I have found out who the Augustus Swineherds are. I must say I consider the institution of village Laureate a fine one and it is so typical of the nobility to maintain such a thing to no benefit of their own. I might seek the man out at some future time and offer him a few literary suggestions.

I learned all this at the vicarage, where I took an early tea and enjoyed a discussion of all manner of things. In London, of course, our conversation would have been considered somewhat pedestrian and lacking in wit, and the topics we discussed would be quite unfashionable, but it is the best I have been able to get here for some time. The vicar remarked that Doyley Silver-Darling would be back in the village for Christmas. 'Indeed,' I said, trying not to show my quickened interest. 'Oh yes,' said Rev. Mullett. 'He always spends the Christmas season with us. He feels he cannot deny people the pleasure of giving him their presents.'

How typically thoughtful of Doyley. I could ask no more on the matter, however, for at that moment the vicar jumped up. 'You must be going,' he said. 'You will obviously want to be home before dark tonight.' Why I should be in such a hurry I did not know but, remembering his warning about April the first, I left at once and came straight home.

Doyley is coming. Now I am truly looking forward to Christmas. But what shall I get him as a present?

****

Locally, 21 December was known as 'the longest night'. As such it was the best night of the year for poaching. Add the need to get meat for the Christmas season, when poaching was outlawed, and it meant that after dark the woods and lanes of the village would be full of people not wanting to be seen. It's unlikely that any of them would have harmed a passerby, but no doubt the vicar thought it best to be safe.

Sid: My Uncle George always reckoned the longest night was the best bit in the whole of Christmas. He said after that you could feel the days drawing out, and before you knew it you could only poach or whatever in unsocial hours.

There was a lot of competition on the longest night to see who could poach the most before dawn. The best that was ever done was years ago in the days when they used to drive flocks of birds to market on foot. Someone managed to poach a whole flock of turkeys which was being driven from Gimingham to Norwich. They was late setting off, so they'd only got as far as St Just the first night and they parked them overnight in a layby on the Trans-Norfolk Highway. Someone had the lot.

143

22 December, Thursday

Last night seemed unbearably long. I simply could not get to sleep until I had decided what to get Doyley as a present. It was well into the small hours when I came up with the solution and finally sank into the arms of Morpheus.

First, there was the problem of familiarity. I have met Doyley several times and hold him in the greatest affection, which I have every hope may be reciprocated. To the rest of the world, however, we are not close friends. Therefore I could not give him anything of an intimate nature. Then there was the matter of expense. Even if I could afford it I could not give him anything too lavish. Not only would that be vulgar, but it might also be misunderstood by others.

In the end, after many hours of tossing and turning, it came to me that, whatever the present, it would be but a token of my true feelings. The nature of the gift itself is unimportant. As Uncle Wesley used to say: 'It is the tobacco that counts.'

So I have bought Doyley a box of cigarettes from nearby Trunch. Miss Trust always smoked a brand called Capstan Full Strength, and I was surprised and delighted to be able to get some so far from Town. To the world it will be a simple gift such as any acquaintance might give another. But Doyley, sensitive aristocrat that he is, will see through the simple cigarettes to the gold mono-grammed cigarette case that I would really wish to give him. Later, on reflection, he will no doubt read the message I would have had inscribed inside.

Later:

This evening there was a great caterwauling in the lane. Maud called out 'It's the wassailers', so I looked through the curtains and quickly realised the derivation of the term. It is clearly a corruption of 'wastrels'. Indeed, that describes exactly what I saw out of the window: a corruption of wastrels, holding out some sort of wooden bowl and bawling a parody of song. 'Wassail, wassail,' they slurred, 'bring out the wassail.'

'Shall I get the bucket of cold water to throw?' asked Maud. 'No,' I replied. 'It is the season of good will to all men. Just tell them to go away at once and never come back.' I am really beginning to feel the spirit of Christmas.

****

144

Sid Kipper believes that Mrs Prewd got the derivation of the term 'wassail' hopelessly wrong:

> That actually comes from the time of the Romans. You see, before then people didn't have no beer. They used to drink all sorts of other things instead. Like wine or mead, or Babycham – or anything they could get their hands on.
>
> Anyhow, along come the Romans and they invented beer. And then they wanted to show off to people about it, so they used to have a big party before Christmas and they used to say, in Roman, of course, 'Do you want to come and have a glass of ale along of me?' And the reply to that would be 'Wha's ale?' And people got hold of the idea that if you went round to someone's house and said 'Wassail', which is Roman for 'Wha's ale?' then they'd give you some to drink. The singing just sort of followed on naturally.

24 December, Saturday

Today my dream of a quiet Christmas has been shattered beyond my wildest nightmares. It all started at some unearthly hour when I was woken by an unholy din. It came from the lane below my bedroom window. Eager to see the source of such a row I threw off the counterpane, leapt to my feet, slipped on my slippers, pulled on a dressing gown, powdered my nose, dabbed on a sprinkling of rose water, applied a dash of rouge and rushed to the window.

I was just in time to see the last of a motley band of louts marching up the lane, carrying lanterns. They were extracting an assortment of vulgar sounds from what I hesitate to describe as musical instruments. Indignant at being woken at what the church clock clearly showed to be 6.45, I summoned Maud. She eventually appeared, yawning and rubbing her eyes, enquiring whether something was the matter. I replied that something was indeed the matter and demanded to know who were those brigands making such a nuisance?

Maud said they were the village Waits. 'If you look now ma'am you'll just see old Herbert's barrow going past.' Back at the window I was indeed able to see, following in the wake of the Waits,

145

Maud's awful brother Albert pushing a dilapidated wheelbarrow. In the barrow sat an old man with a sort of bag at his feet. Attached to this was a tube, rather like the one we had in London to talk to the servants without having to see them. This led to a kind of pipe with holes in, which seemed to be some distant relative of the flute or clarinet.

The man, who I took to be Herbert, was pushing on the bag with his foot and endeavouring to shape notes on the instrument with his hands. At this point the ruffian glanced upwards and I hastily stepped back and drew the curtain, lest he catch sight of me in my dressing gown.

From then on the day has been one long round of activities, all of a decidedly pagan nature. The natives have pulled vast amounts of greenery through the lanes. This afternoon Constable Crabb could be seen pedalling past the house in hot pursuit of an escaping goose and I have had to see off three separate groups of carol singers. Even as I write, some time after returning from the midnight service, the lane is still busy with revellers from The Goat Inn, singing what sound like carols. They are not any carols that I know, however.

****

Herbert Kipper was in his seventies in 1904, so it's perhaps not surprising that he needed pushing around in a barrow. However, that was not the main reason for his mode of transport. The Trunch Blowpipes are played by means of a bag of air being squeezed with the foot, so it's difficult to play them while marching. Herbert – known as Dirty Herbert – has been called 'the last of the great blowpipers', but Sid Kipper, who plays the instrument himself, hotly disputes this. 'I'm just as good as old Dirty was. I'll challenge him to a piping contest any time he likes,' declares Sid loudly and regularly. As Herbert died in 1908 Sid's claim appears quite safe.

O little town of Gimingham, how still we see thee sleep,
As through thy dark streets and onto the roofs a hooded figure
    creeps,
He climbs down all your chimneys, he carries a large sack,
He fills it with your valuables, then quickly hurries back.

In the bleak midwinter the frosty milkmaids moan;
Udders hard as iron, like getting blood from a stone.
Snow had fallen, snow on snow on snow on snow on snow (on
    snow),
In the bleak midwinter and not so long ago.

O Polly and Ivy, now they are both full grown,
Of all the girls who live round here the boys won't leave them
    alone.
With the rising of the sap and the running of the blood,
The playing of the merry organ, sweet singing all in the pub.

Good King Wenceslas look out! It is the feast of Steven.
There's some funny folk about – crooks and madmen even!
Wenceslas was feeling bright, watching snowflakes glister,
Till a poor man came in sight, completely spoiled the vista.

While shepherds watched their flocks by night they started for
    to think:
'It's cold and wet and miserable, let's go and have a drink.'
The servant of the lord come down before they had got back,
He went and told his master and got them all the sack.
(*O Little Town Of Gimingham*)

25 December, Sunday

Early this morning I hung the Christmas wreath on the front door.
Later, however, I was forced to remove it again. It seems that people
hereabouts are unaware of this civilised custom and I grew tired of
them calling to ask who had died. So now we have no seasonal
decoration at all.

Maud had been plaguing me to allow her to decorate the
house in accordance with local traditions, but her description caused
me to refuse immediately. It involves too much greenery, including

147

holly, with which, I gather, we should deck the hall. This seemed especially impractical, as our tiny hall is already almost filled by Uncle Wesley's elephant's foot umbrella stand.

For our Christmas dinner – which was perversely served at luncheon – Maud brought in a gigantic turkey. Matters became rather indelicate when Maud proceeded to offer me a choice between 'breast' and 'leg'. My late husband would have found such a choice impossible, especially when offered by a young girl as cheaply obvious as Maud. I am not myself used to choosing in these circumstances. I am used to a man carving and giving me what he thinks inappropriate. Eventually I made it clear that I wished to have nothing to do with either breast or leg, but would have some other part. I ended up with something called the 'parson's nose', which was very unappetising and rather greasy. At least it was aptly named.

This afternoon, Maud having gone off to spend the rest of the day with her family at Box Cottage, I delivered Doyley's present. Inside I had slipped a note, suggesting that he might like to call on Tuesday, during what I understand is the customary alms-giving tour of the village. I was forced to surrender it to the underfootman, who told me the family were not receiving visitors. Sounds of revelry came from both upstairs and downstairs, as they did from many a house on my way home. I persuaded myself, as I sat at home alone, that I was lucky to be away from all such tomfoolery.

****

Sid: A lot of people don't know why we have turkey at Christmas, so I'll tell you. That all go back to the Iceni, who used to worship this mythical bird just like a turkey. They do say that in North Norfolk there's a giant turkey carved into a hillside, but I've never seen it. Come to think of it, I've never seen a hillside in North Norfolk.

Anyhow, the real turkey was brought to Norfolk by a nun called Brenda, who accidentally discovered Mexico whilst on a pilgrimage to Lourdes. She brought back the turkeys and at first people kept them as pets. The only trouble was they grew a bit big and used to get underfoot in them small cottages. Especially if you had visitors. So one Christmas, when someone had relatives coming, they said 'What shall we do with the turkey?' And someone else said 'stick it in the oven, out of the way'. So they did, and when someone else again lit the oven without looking inside they invented roast turkey for Christmas. Of course, they'd discovered stuffing a long time before that.

26 December, Monday

Today has seen a veritable procession of tradesmen and other vermin calling for their Christmas boxes. 'I've a good mind to give you a box around the ears,' I told one, who was dressed in his shabby best and claimed to be a builder. 'I don't mind where you put it, Missus,' he replied, 'but that's my due for rendering serviced over the past twelvemonth. Here's my cap in my hand and I'll thank you to fill it for me.' This I gladly did, filling it with his head until it came down over his eyes. After that I did box his ears and his rather prominent nose too, for good measure, and propelled him in the direction of the lane. There he staggered rather comically for ten minutes or so, until another of his kind came and led him home. I was troubled by no more callers.

This evening Maud returned from her family. She demonstrated how fast news travels in a backwater such as this, for she knew all about my present to Doyley. Although I took trouble not to show it I was almost pleased to see her, not least because she cooked me what passes for a decent meal in these parts. I had been forced to eat a luncheon of cold turkey, which I can assure you is a most unpleasant experience.

****

As so often when my researches have involved Doyley Silver-Darling, the memoirs of his faithful retainer, Herring, have proved invaluable:

> At Christmas we always went up from London to St Just-near-Trunch. My master greatly enjoyed these visits, as He could drink and sport in a manner which might be thought unseemly in the Capital. 'Herring,' He would cry, 'this country air gives a chap an appetite. Pass me another ruddy pheasant, peasant.' This was His Lordship's idea of wit.
>
> One year He was having an affair with one of the village girls, whose mistress would rarely allow her out. On the afternoon of Christmas Day, the girl herself arrived unexpectedly, and my master was delighted. 'Look Herring!' He exclaimed. 'The old prude has sent me a Christmas present. Push off for the rest of the day, will you. I must unwrap my present and play with it at once.'

149

Later, however, I was forced to interrupt His play, as a genuine present had been delivered by the girl's mistress. When unwrapped this proved to be a packet of cigarettes, with a note which he looked at in great puzzlement. 'I've no idea what she's trying to tell me,' He said, 'but I shall certainly call on Tuesday.' With that He dismissed me again and I spent a very pleasant Christmas with the staff.

(*I Did It*: Chapter 4 – His Master's Vice)

The affair between Doyley and Maud was not simply a case of the future Lord of the Manor having his feudal rights over a village girl. The custom of droit de sinecure, or the right to an easy life, still applied to the landed gentry, but they could not simply pick girls as their bed warmers. They were expected to stick to one at a time. Maud, however, was different. She was as eager as Doyley. Of course, she could never expect to marry him. Her father, old Dan Kipper, would never have allowed it. The Kippers were a proud family and marriage to the local landowner would have destroyed the family tradition of poaching, as they couldn't be seen to be living off their in-laws. So although the pair loved each other, theirs was always fated to be a private passion.

27 December, Tuesday

What shame! What indignity! I can hardly bring myself to think about what has happened. My position in the village is now even more intolerable than it already was.

The day started so well, with a thrill of anticipation. A note came first thing, saying that Doyley would indeed call today during the round of alms-giving. I was overjoyed.

Sure enough, this afternoon a great procession turned into the lane. At its head was a huge and fearsome beast, which Maud told me was the Silver-Darling's prize bull. It was bedecked with silver ornaments and led by a liveried hand. Next came Doyley, on a great white charger, wearing the uniform of an honorary Captain of the Mundesley Dark Infantry. Then came two columns of family retainers, carrying the bags of alms, flanking a landau. In this sat Lady Silver-Darling, waving to either side, and veritably dripping with gems and jewellery of all kinds. In London she would have looked vulgar, but here it seemed fitting, reassuring the peasantry that all is well with the world. The rear was brought up by a team of bullocks, drawing a huge cannon, which the family won during the Crimean Wars, in a card game with the Duke of Norfolk.

Up the lane they processed, stopping at the alms houses, where the pathetic denizens gratefully grabbed the presents which Her Ladyship so graciously gave them. Eventually the head of the column drew level with my gate and Doyley dismounted. When I went to the gate to receive him he stepped to one side, took a bag from one of the retainers and before I could divine his intent he had presented the bag to me! 'I had not realised you were a distressed gentlewoman until I got your present,' he said, 'but since you asked us to call here is a little something to bring you joy this festive season.' With that he sprang to the saddle and rode on.

I was devastated. How could such a misunderstanding have occurred? How could he humiliate me so in front of the entire village? I ran into the house, stupidly clutching the bag he had given me and every inch the distressed gentlewoman. That, of course, could not be allowed to last long. My eye fell upon Uncle Wesley's favourite bludgeon, standing proud and firm in the corner, and his last utterance as he lay dying in agony came back to me: 'Stiff upper lip, old girl; stiff upper lip!' At the time I rather resented the fact that he chose to address these last words to his mastiff, rather than to me, but now I drew strength from them. I opened the bag to see what it contained and out leaped three foul.

'Three french hens,' exclaimed Maud, entering without knocking. 'All we need now is a cock,' I muttered and I could swear that she said something like 'Speak for yourself.' Even beating her for her impertinence did not lift my black mood.

However, writing this has helped to calm me and now a marvellous thought has occurred. Is there not a piece of doggerel which begins 'On the first day of Christmas my true love sent to me', and do not three french hens feature in it? Perhaps Doyley was replying to the message of my cigarettes whilst pretending to the village that we have no connection. It is a wonderful thought, but I must keep it to myself for the time being, as he leaves for London again tomorrow.

****

151

The giving of alms on the day after Boxing Day has been a duty of the Lord of the Manor of St Just-near-Trunch for centuries. Years ago gifts were given on Boxing Day not from the greater to the lesser, but the other way round, as a form of tribute. The Lord received many unwanted gifts and he would travel around the village the next day, giving them to whoever he met. We find the following in the manorial records for 1672:

Alms given this day:

To Gabriel Artichoke, Cobler:	A pair of hose of an exceptionally vulgar pattern.
To Theodore Elvette, Blind beggar:	A volume of fupposedly witty and amusing prose, wherein the Grate and Famouf tell of their most amusing experiences involving the plague.
To Frederick Carter, Carter:	A boxe of dubious fweetmeats, most tastelessly wrapped.
To Edith Pilchard, Spinster:	A divice, or gadgette, wherewith one may remove the ftonnes from the hoofs of a horse.
To various others:	Much moor of the fame.

Over the centuries the Silver-Darling family realised that this was a chance to get rid of all sorts of unwanted items and would ceremonially hand out cast offs to a peasantry who were forced to appear grateful. In those days before reliable contraception unwanted children were even given on some occasions. These were known as 'babes in alms'.

All in all Mrs Prewd was lucky to get three french hens, though I'm forced to wonder what was wrong with them.

28 December, Wednesday

I woke this morning with very mixed feelings. After the events of yesterday I am now unsure whether my position in the village is as desperate as I first thought or whether, as I thought later, it only seems that way, whilst in fact being quite different. It is difficult to know how to proceed.

I happened to say to Maud this morning that it was a pity Doyley Silver-Darling had to return to London so early in the Christmas season. I was surprised by her reply. 'Oh, he'll have been out of the village before dawn,' she said, 'before the Lord could get after him.' Why on earth, I enquired, should his father wish to pursue him? She looked at me as if I was the one of limited intelligence. 'Not his father,' she said. 'I mean the Lord of Miss Rule.' I quickly demonstrated what nonsense she was talking with the aid of a handy olive branch. I informed her that I was aware of no Miss Rule living in the area and I would take my walk. 'You must do what you like,' she pouted, 'but I don't think you'll like it.'

Outside the ground was frozen solid, with all the puddles turned to ice. I was forced to pick my way with great care, watching my footing at all times. Proceeding in this manner I was unaware of the approach of another person until the irregular rhythm of his gait was quite close. At once I knew that tread. It was the wooden-legged triplets of Maud's unspeakable brother, Albert. They stopped directly in front of me, leaving their owner blocking my advance along the narrow lane.

'Out of my way,' I said firmly. 'I think I have made my feelings towards you clear enough in the past.' He showed no sign of moving, however, and indeed had the audacity to address me. 'Heave to a moment,' he slurred, for he had clearly been drinking. 'You and me must parley. I have been chosen by my shipmates to be Lord of Misrule or as I prefer it, Admiral of Misrule. I may choose whoever I like to be my Lady for the day and I choose you. You cannot gainsay me, for I have custom on my side. We must lead the revels, splice the mainbrace and devil take the kidneys.'

He went on in this ludicrous fashion for some time, but I did not stay to hear it all. I knocked his wooden leg from under him with my stick. As he grovelled for it in the snow I returned home and remained there.

****

The custom of allowing a commoner to 'rule' for a day at Christmas is found all over the country. Boy Bishops were elected in some parts; others had the King and Queen of the Bean! Mrs Prewd, not for the first time, defied convention by refusing to be the Lady of Misrule. The Lord could choose any woman he found on the streets of the village as his consort for the day's revels.

The Lord had great powers for the day and local worthies tended to lock themselves away for the duration. They would otherwise become prime targets for mischief and no doubt this is why Doyley Silver-Darling had left the village early.

The revels involved much drinking and whatever pranks the Lord could devise. The quality of the day depended very much on the wit of the Lord. He was selected by the drawing of lots, although this was restricted to the labouring classes after one farmer decided that it would be a huge joke to have all the village picking stones from his fields all day, in ten degrees of frost.

Sid: I never got to be Lord. Well, you see, whenever I drew lots, someone else drew lots more, so I didn't get the job. Not that I wanted it. You have to keep thinking and deciding what to do all the time, sort of making your mind up. Well, I made my mind up years ago, thank you, and I don't want to have to go through that again.

When Great Uncle Albert was Lord he had sports and all sorts of races. He won the three-legged race, of course. But people always reckon he was good at Lording. He's remembered for it. Even today you can go up to someone in the village and say 'Do you remember Albert Kipper?' and more likely than not they'll say 'Good Lord!'

30 December, Friday

Christmas goes on here at full tilt. Today, Maud tells me, the pantomime begins at the Trunch Empire music hall. They are presenting, I gather, 'Big Dick Whittington', with the title role being taken by Jimmy 'Am I Boring You' Kipper. I shall make a point of avoiding the production as one would the plague. The entertainments of the common people are invariably in poor taste, and there are none so common, poor or tasteless as the inhabitants of St Just-near-Trunch.

I came across a pathetic example of their type this afternoon. It was on my way to the vicarage, to call on Rev. Mullett. I thought

154

I might sound him out about my position in the village after the alms-giving business. As I passed through the village a shadowy figure beckoned to me from an alley. Taking a firm grip on my umbrella I walked straight on. Nevertheless this scruffy individual emerged from the alley, carrying a cake tin, and addressed me in a low voice. 'Want to buy any mince pies, lady?' he asked, his eyes flicking about nervously. 'A quid a piece, and no questions asked.' A question sprang to my mind immediately, that question being 'How would you like a good solid clip around the ear?' I did not ask it. Instead, I ascertained the answer by experiment and found he did not like it one bit.

On arrival I asked the vicar about the incident, but he simply shifted his quid of tobacco from one cheek to the other. 'We do not discuss such matters here at the vicarage, Mrs Prewd,' was all he would say on the matter. I did broach the subject of my position, but he did not seem to know what I was talking about. I take this to mean that the matter is of less consequence than I had feared.

****

Nowadays we think nothing of buying mince pies over the counter or carrying them openly through the streets. It's hard to imagine them as objects of excitement, mystery and subversion, but they were once just that. It was the Puritans who identified the mince pie as a focus of pagan worship. In 1656 Fletcher wrote:

> Idolatrie in crust! Babylone's whore
> Rak'd from the grave and baked by hanches, then
> Sew'd up in Coffins to unholy men;
> Defil'd, with superstition, like the Gentiles
> Of old, that worship'd onions, roots and lentiles! *

This particular rhyme caused great consternation in the Trunch area at the time, not just because of its attack on the mince pie, but also because of the reference to root worship, which was common. A whole culture had been built up around the root, including roots music and rituals for finding your roots, both of which are currently enjoying something of a revival.

Sid: The Puritans was held bent on stopping people enjoying themselves. They banned a whole load of things, including dancing round the maypole and mince pies. Which is why you don't never see no one dancing around the mince pies nowadays.

155

Then they had these Constables of the Watch – which is where they get the saying 'If you want to know the time ask a policeman'. Ours was called Constable Joy and he was a miserable bugger. They had a saying about him, too. They used to say 'There will be no more joy till there is no more Joy.' That was their idea of a joke in them days. Well, the Puritans wouldn't let you have anything funnier than that in case you enjoyed it.

In Mrs Prewd's time the mince pie was still frowned on by the local establishment, leading to a thriving black market. It's often the case that when something is banned it becomes all the more popular. This was true, for instance, during the period of prohibition in America, when killing people was outlawed, leading at once to an outbreak of mass murder by the likes of Al Capone.

Some of the mince pies produced in St Just-near-Trunch were hardly less lethal, being made in squalid little underground bakeries. Records of the time suggest that they made extremely poor eating, although it seems they were quite adequate for dancing around.

* From *The Englishman's Christmas*, by J. A. R. Pimlott. Published in 1978 by The Harvester Press, Sussex.

31 December, Saturday

The fact that what all decent people call New Year's Eve is known hereabouts as Old Year's Night is typical of their insistence on living in the past. Aside from Farmer Trout's track tor, which he never seems to use, there is not a single sign hereabouts that the nineteenth century has arrived, let alone departed again. Coming here has been like a giant step back in time, to the days when life was short, brutish and nasty, and the peasantry even shorter, considerably more brutish and decidedly nastier. Even the urchins of the city streets have more wit than their country cousins. The imminence of the year of Our Lord, nineteen hundred and five – the fifth year of a new century and the fourth of our new King – has little significance here. It simply presages another twelve months exactly like the last.

For me, in contrast, it brings the dawn of a new life. In a little under three months I shall leave this place behind me for ever. Until that glorious day, however, I shall keep this diary as I have promised. Perhaps one day it will serve as a measure of my suffering.

Today passed rather quietly and I began to think we might have done with the goings on of Christmas. However, as Uncle Wesley was wont to say, 'The brightest hour is just before dusk.' So it proved. As night fell people began to skulk about the lanes and at one point a tall dark man who I did not recognise passed the house. When I asked Maud who he might be she replied that he might be anyone, but that he was in fact A Tall Dark Stranger. How a stranger can have capital letters I do not know, but that is how Maud pronounced it. A little later he actually came to the door, with a lump of coal in his hand, of all things. I firmly informed him that I was not in the habit of purchasing fuel from itinerant beggars in the middle of the night and gave him a black eye to increase his darkness.

At midnight, as the church clock rang out the chimes for a quarter to seven, Maud turned to me and cried 'Happy one hundred and twelve, Mrs Prewd.' The poor, ignorant creature does not even know what year it is, let alone what day.

****

Maud Kipper was actually quite correct in her calculation of the year – from a local point of view. As I've explained elsewhere, Trunch was at the time still allied with revolutionary France and at war with England. They naturally used the French Revolutionary calendar. In the Parish Records the adoption of this new calendar was marked with a simple, single dot. This became known as 'the year dot' and the period following it as 'A.D.' or 'After Dot'.

1 January 1905, Sunday

New Year's Day – or Old Year's Morn, as it is known hereabouts – arrived as a dull, overcast misery of a day. Perhaps the weather sympathised with my mood. Perhaps Maud did too, as she sang a dirge-like song: 'Oh it's many a dark and a cloudy morning turns out to be a dank, dark cloudy day.' In fact the whole village seemed subdued as I made my way to church. Almost every man I met was holding his head and moaning, as if some divine justice had passed through the streets giving each of them the blow to the head which they so richly deserve.

My depression was caused by yesterday's thoughts of London. Although the business of the alms giving seems to have been forgotten, I am still unsettled here. Three months seems like a very long time, yet that is how much longer I must remain in this filthy place.

The filth is currently covered over by a crisp, clean covering of snow, of which I heartily approve. I said as much to Farmer Trout, whom I met in the lane this afternoon. He had clearly been drinking.

'All very well for you,' he slurred, 'but it makes it very difficult for people to get about.' I told him I had found the roads in the village to be quite passable, but he was not to be mollified. 'You've got to think wider than just the village,' he replied. 'The Trans-Norfolk Highway is totally blocked.' I dismissed the man, telling him he was making the story up to disguise his own inebriation. I pride myself on my knowledge of geography and I am sure I would have heard of such a road had it existed.

As Uncle Wesley used to say: 'There's many an English drunkard on the rolling English road.'

****

I must admit that I had never heard of the Trans-Norfolk Highway either, until I asked Sid about it.

Sid: The reason you haven't heard of it is because it's not called that on the maps. On the maps it's called the B1145. It runs from coast to coast in North Norfolk, from Kings Lynn to Mundesley.

Of course, years ago it used to go beyond Mundesley to the coastal village of Understrand. We used to have the three strands

159

– Overstrand, Sidestrand and Understrand. But Understrand isn't on the coast any more: it's under the coast. It all happened when they had these new sea defences. They was very proud of them, you see, so when they had a visit from the Lord Tennant of Norfolk they said 'Excuse us, your Tennantship, but would you like to open our new sea defences.' So he did. And that was the last that was ever seen of the village of Understrand.

But they do say that if you stand on Mundesley beach on a dark moonlit night, with a high tide, you can still hear the bells of Understrand church, ringing in the steeple as the waves pass over it. And they also reckon, if the wind is in the right direction, you can hear the ghostly voices of the villagers, all arguing about who's fault it was.

5 January, Thursday

My depression of Sunday alarmed me. For a time I feared I might be catching the disease of self-pity from the locals, so I was delighted to be taken ill on Tuesday. This also afforded me the luxury of missing the continuing celebrations of Christmas, which now seem to have blurred into one long, noisy, drunken turmoil.

I think my malady may have been caused by the sudden thaw. Whatever the reason, for the last two days I have been confined to my bed with some sort of ague. I felt so bad yesterday morning that I asked Maud to send for the doctor. By the evening he had still not arrived, so when Maud brought my beef tea I accused her of failing to carry out my instruction. 'I did send for him,' she protested. 'Then why,' I enquired, 'has he not arrived?' 'Oh, he never comes if you send for him. He reckon that if you're ill enough to send for him you'll make the effort to go to the surgery.'

I was too weak to reply.

✱✱✱✱✱✱✱✱✱✱

Dr Dabb was one of the old school of doctors. His favourite prescription was 'Pull yourself together', and his second favourite was three months hard labour, which he handed out as a magistrate. His surgery was in North Walsham and generally people had to go there to see him. Once a month he did spend a day in St Just-near-Trunch, but never announced which day it was going to be, so it was difficult to be ill at the right time to take advantage

160

of the visit. In fact he only made the trip to attend to the needs of the Silver-Darlings. They, of course, were not told to pull themselves together. Neither were they prescribed hard labour – even if caught red-handed. It was Dr Dabb's opinion that the nobility were highly strung, like thoroughbreds and should therefore be treated with rest and self-indulgence.

Mrs Prewd might well have approved of Dr Dabb's attitudes, but as far as I can tell they never met. However, on this occasion she helped prove him right. She pulled herself together and recovered almost immediately.

The sun had set behind the hill, across the weary moor,
When weary and lame a boy there came up to a doctor's door.
Can you tell me where e'er there be one who can me assist,
To cure my ills, prescribe my pills, and be a pharmacist?

My father's dead, my mother too, and I'm not too well myself,
So I'd be glad if you could spare some medicine from your shelf.
If I can stop inside you shop, out of the fog and mist,
I'll work by day to earn my pay and be a pharmacist.

The doctor's wife said 'Cure the lad, he seems so pale and sick.'
'Yes, father do,' cried his daughter dear. 'These pills should do the
    trick.
Don't make him go out in the snow, I really must insist,
But let him stay and earn his pay and be a pharmacist.'

The man that was a boy is now assistant in the shop,
But as pharmacist's assistant he was not prepared to stop.
And often he'd look at the poisons book, and see there in the list,
That there's many a potion to aid his notion to be a pharmacist.

So it was not surprising when the poor old couple died;
Which left the boy the business, and the daughter for a bride.
A knowing gleam in his eye was seen, as bride and bridegroom
    kissed –
'Blast me,' said he. 'Now that's the way to be a pharmacist.'
(*The Pharmacist*)

6 January, Friday

Today I feel much better and received my first visitor. Rev. Mullett's bedside manner leaves something to be desired, I must say. Amongst other things he asked a number of tactless questions about my preferences for funeral services. If I did not think better of him I might believe that I saw disappointment in his eyes on hearing of my recovery.

After the vicar had left, Maud made me comfortable and then went out for the evening. She claims it is something called Twelfth Night. The correct appellation, I told her, is Epiphany. 'That's right,' she said. 'That's Latin for Twelfth Night.' There seemed little point in arguing with her. I am trying to restore my energies and will not waste them on such a lost cause.

****

Twelfth Night was the last big celebration of the Christmas season. It's probably not worth detailing the revels here, since they were much like other revels. There was drinking, singing, more drinking, some dancing, some more drinking, and so on until the drink or the legs gave out. It was a time of mingled joy and sorrow, sometimes known as the Chinese New Year, due to its sweet and sour nature.

10 January, Tuesday

Things are at last getting back to normal after Christmas. At least, they are getting back to what passes for normal in these peculiar parts.

This afternoon the hunt met at The New Goat Inn. When Maud and I arrived, however, there was neither rider nor horse in sight. Maud explained it was their custom to meet inside the inn for a stirrup cup and suggested we join them there. I assured her that before I sank so low as to be seen dead in that den of utter iniquity I would turn in my grave, but I think she failed to understand.

Before I could spell it out simply to her, the hunt began to emerge from the bar, the horses having some difficulty in negotiating the step. What a glorious sight they were, in their coats of hunting red – which is, in fact, a delicate pink – and their high hats.

It seemed that all the local gentry were there, but only one stood out for me. Doyley Silver-Darling was at his most grand, his most handsome, his most noble. Between his thighs was a huge, proud, steaming stallion and on his lips a snarl of contempt for the rest of the world. Would he notice us, I wondered, standing there below him? At that very moment his gaze fell upon us, and he smiled. I have to confess that my heart began to flutter like that of a silly girl. For a moment it almost seemed that it was a silly girl, Maud, that he was smiling at. It may be that he has a slight squint, for I have noticed a similar thing before.

For the rest of the day I felt the warmth of that smile suffusing me, as we followed the hunt, helping to put down fallen horses and their riders.

****

Sid: Course, the real reason for hunting is nothing to do with catching anything. The real reason is to get cold and wet and miserable so you have an excuse to get in the pub for some serious drinking afterwards, and have a good sing. That's toffs for you – in our family we leave out the cold, wet and miserable bit.

Sometimes they used to have a drag hunt. Now that was a laugh, that was. All the men used to dress up as women and vice versa. They used to say that if you hadn't seen Lord Silver-Darling in full skirts, riding side-saddle, then you hadn't lived.

12 January, Thursday

Tonight we held this year's first meeting of the Trunch Musical Appreciation Society. I was sad that Doyley could not attend because of saddle sores, but Mr Babcock was our host and we listened to a selection of improving music on his new machine. I fear our discussion was not of the highest grade, however. Mr Babcock had such profound insights as: 'I liked the bits where it went dum de dum the best,' and, 'That da capo bit really goes to the head, doesn't it?'

Miss Pickerel was not much better. She has obviously read a book on musical criticism, but it has taught her nothing. Of course, that was probably not the fault of the book. As Uncle Wesley would say: 'You can't tell a book by its reader.' She offered gems like: 'Do you not feel that the harmonic counterpoint of the central section appertains to the pastoral side of man's nature, while the staccato cadenza reflects a more urban nuance?' The confidence with which she delivered this would have been more justified if she had been facing the machine. Then she would have seen that the sounds she referred to were those of Mr Babcock sharpening the needle.

These are early days, however. The whole point of the Society is to elevate such people. I only hope that our new members, the Misses Norris, were not put off. They are twin spinsters, of the hale and hearty type. Very sporting. They spend much of their time doing good works in Northrepps, though I venture to say that anyone visiting Northrepps would find little evidence of their labours. Nevertheless, they are of good stock, and although one has a 'tin ear' and the other is tone deaf I dare say they will find that no handicap in our little Society.

****

Miss Pickerel, before her departure for Germany, donated her books to the Coote Memorial Museum, hoping they might form the basis of a lending library. The project was actually started, but as no one in the area wanted to borrow any of her books it was quickly stopped again. Now they lie, gathering dust, in a back room. There I found the very book which Miss Pickerel may have read in her attempt to appreciate music. *Grave's Golden Treasury of Music* may never have been a best seller, but it makes fascinating reading today, 90 years after its publication. Here is an extract from the introduction:

MUSICAL APPRECIATION
Classical music is the sort that is listened to by decent people in evening dress. It is played by rather dubious people in evening dress. Some conductors are decent enough people, especially those who retain their amateur status, but it is best to treat them all with caution to begin with.

It is important to select the right composers. Those whose names begin with a B or an S are generally safe (Beethoven and Bach; Schubert and Schumann). Do not be put off by funny foreign names. These are compulsory for composers and even English composers have them (Holst and Delius). The only decent composers with English names are foreigners (Grainger), dead (Spencer) or hyphenated (Vaughan-Williams).

The way to appreciate music for the beginner is to watch others. If they seem to like it then it is correct to praise it; if not it is best to say nothing. If the audience is divided in its response remember that Knights count double, Peers treble and Royalty out-vote everyone else put together.
(George Grave, March 1899)

You can imagine how little this would have prepared Miss Pickerel for the intellectual life of the Trunch Musical Appreciation Society!

13 January, Friday

Following the relative civilisation of last night's meeting, today's events have only served to demonstrate once more how far removed I am from the life I would be living in London.

It seems that, for some reason, when the thirteenth of the month falls on a Friday it is considered an unlucky day. As Maud put it: 'Best you don't do nothing today that you want to come out well, for no good never come from no Friday the thirteenth.' I quickly demonstrated how right she was by giving her a short, sharp lesson on the abuse of the negative.

I have seen before that these people are dreadfully superstitious and today has been but a further revelation. People all over the village were touching wood or throwing salt over their shoulders and the sweep was doing a fine trade, charging sixpence a time to touch him. I decided to set a firm example and show what nonsense this all was. Seeing a man working on a ladder I went over and deliberately walked underneath it. This immediately had the desired effect as people gasped – surprised, no doubt, that I was not immediately struck down by ill fortune.

The man on the ladder was so astonished that he lost his grip and might have suffered a nasty injury had he not been lucky enough to have his fall broken by one of the gawping bystanders. Which, I felt, only went to prove my point.

****

Mrs Prewd was quite right, for once. The people of St Just, like rural folk the world over, were extremely superstitious. This is not really so very odd. Their lives were ruled by things over which they had no control, such as the

165

seasons, the weather and the state of Lady Silver-Darling's gout. **Not** surprising, then, that they felt at the mercy of the fates.

Sid: There was three sorts of luck. There was good luck, bad luck and
no luck at all. For instance, if a black cat crossed your path that
was good luck. If you ran over it then that was bad luck. And if Mrs
Dace saw you do it that was no luck at all, 'cause that was her cat.
    Some people believed in the luck of the drawer. Old Cyril
Cockle, he was one. 'That's the luck of the drawer,' he used to say,
and to make sure of it he always carried an old drawer around with
him. People used to poke fun at him, but he din't give a fiddler's
dram. He used to say: 'As long as I've had this old drawer with me
I've never been struck by lightning, so I aren't going to take the
chance of it happening now.' And do you know, it never did.

17 January , Tuesday

I have received an invitation to dine at the Great Hall. I am a little unclear about the occasion. The invitation mentions Lady Silver-Darling's great-aunt, Grace, who I have never met. Can she still be alive? I shall find out more on Thursday, when we dine.

18 January, Wednesday

This morning I went to North Walsham to buy a dress for tomorrow's dinner. I have to admit that I got a little carried away – no thanks to the train, which was three and a half minutes late leaving Trunch Central Station. I found a delightful little shop, managed by a Mrs Braithwaite and called 'Mr Braithwaite's' after its owner.

What a morning I had, trying on dresses and telling the manageress about last year's London fashions. How hard it was to choose. I decided that the dress must not be too daring, lest it shock Lady Silver-Darling's great-aunt and finally settled on black, with chiffon sleeves and trimmings, and feathers on the bodice. I shall wear it with my jet.

On my return to Trunch Central darkness was falling and I cast about for a porter. I eventually found one hiding behind a pile of boxes. I encouraged him, by the method of carrot and stick, to carry my packages to the Old Toll House. On our arrival, however,

Maud informed me that we did not actually have a carrot in the house, so he would have to be satisfied with a parsnip. I hope the great-aunt appreciates all the trouble I have gone to.

****

Mrs Prewd needn't have worried about Grace Silver-Darling's approval. The lady in question had been dead for two and a half decades. She was, however, a great heroine to the Silver-Darling Family and an annual dinner was held in her memory.

There isn't space here to do full justice to Grace's heroic tale – how her father, fallen on hard times, had taken a cottage near Cromer lighthouse, believing this would make him exempt from inland revenue demands; how she set off from the lighthouse in a tiny dingy; how she rowed for an hour into the teeth of a gale; how she finally arrived at the town centre and collected the groceries herself, thus shaming the shopkeeper who had claimed that it was impossible to deliver that day because of the weather. The story is well enough known, anyway.

Grace's deed was the talk of the upper classes, who said that it just went to prove that standards of service were slipping and the nobility were made of sterner stuff. When she was called up to the Palace to receive a special award the whole family was proud. Grace Silver-Darling's medal still stands on the mantelpiece at the Great Hall. On one side is the head of Queen Victoria and on the other an inscription: 'For Determination In The Face Of Rotten Service', with a picture of St Just, the patron saint of futile gestures. It represents a proud moment in the history of a very proud family.

19 January, Thursday

Dinner tonight was a great success. Grace Silver-Darling was not there, as she has been dead for some years, but I heard all about the great lady. I would have liked to meet such an example to our sex. I said as much to the company and there ensued a considerable conversation about those things which are desirable and admirable in a woman. His Lordship, I am afraid, has lamentably obvious tastes. I imagine the chambermaids go in fear at all times.

Doyley, on the other hand, is more discerning. One cannot imagine him carrying on with a servant. He offered us a description of his perfect woman and as he did so my heart began to beat a little faster. Perhaps I flatter myself, but I feel that terms such as 'mature', 'strong', 'well dressed', 'experienced' and 'witty' might all apply to me. I do believe that there is real hope for us.

As I left Doyley saw me to the door and remarked on my dress. 'Mrs Prewd,' he declared. 'That is a most peculiar dress.' I took him to mean that the dress is unique and suits me especially. The word peculiar does derive, after all, from the Latin 'peculiaris', meaning 'of private property'. My wish that Doyley would make me his private property seems altogether more possible after tonight.

****

Doyley Silver-Darling's description of his ideal woman was a sham. His mother was getting worried, at the time, about his failure to show any sign of producing a legitimate heir. He was very pleased with the way he confused the issue at dinner, as he wrote in a letter that night to Sir Alfred Friend:

Salutations Old Bean,

How are things with you? I say, I've just pulled a really fast one. I've pulled the wool over Mater's eyes good and proper. You know she's always on at me about getting hitched and producing some bouncing little Silver-Darlings to keep the name going? Mind you, I don't see what it's got to do with her – her name was Higgins if I recall.

Look, I'll start another parathing, and see if I can get to the point. At dinner tonight Mother wanted to hear my idea of a perfect woman. Well, I couldn't tell her the truth, could I? I don't know the Latin words for a lot of it. Anyhow, I looked at the dreadful Prune woman – who was here for some reason or other – and she sort of inspired me.

'Mature,' I said. Well, old Prune is more corked than mature. 'Strong,' I said. Prune is certainly a bit strong. 'Well dressed,' I said, noticing her ridiculous costume. 'Experienced,' I said. God knows what experiences Prune has been through, but they have left some nasty scars. 'Witty,' I said finally, looking at the half-witted Prune.

Anyhow, mother seemed delighted and positively purred with approval. Little does she know, eh, Alfie?

Anyhow again, that's quite enough for now.

Doyley.

21 January, Saturday

I returned to North Walsham today, to tell Mrs Braithwaite what a success the dress was. After all, she did try to persuade me against it on Wednesday, so it was my duty to let her know how wrong she was. Maud and I walked together to the station, where I left her to go shopping while I settled myself in a second-class carriage on the 8.47 from Trunch Central. I should perhaps explain that there is no first-class service on this line. The choice is between second class, third class and remedial class.

When 8.53 arrived, with no sign of the train departing, I collared a skulking member of staff and demanded to know why. 'We're waiting for a very important passenger Ma'am,' he replied in a careless manner. I was about to give him something to care about when my attention was distracted by a commotion at the other end of the station. Then Doyley Silver-Darling burst onto the platform, followed by Herring, who was trying to run whilst carrying a mountain of bags and cases. As the servant shoved bags into the guard's van his master strode along the train and, to my great delight, entered my compartment.

Doyley looked magnificent. He was breathing deeply, which caused his manly chest to rise and fall majestically. He pulled out a handkerchief, with M.K. initialled on it, and mopped his brow. Then, looking in the carriage mirror, he used it to remove some red marks from his cheek. Only then did he look around and see me. A variety of emotions seemed to cross his face. 'Oh, Mrs Prewd,' he said. 'We were just talking about you. Sorry to hold the dashed train up, but you know how it is?' I assured him that I did although, in fact, I do not.

How delightful to ride through the countryside with Doyley Silver-Darling all to myself. I think he felt it as well. He was so aware of our closeness that he did not speak, lest he break the spell. It was almost as if we were leaving St Just-near-Trunch behind us, running away to a new life together. If only it could have gone on for ever.

Sadly it went on only as far as North Walsham. I had to leave the train there, while Doyley sped on towards London. His current visit is over and he will not be back till the middle of February. I will miss him, but he will still be here, in my heart. I shall treasure his last words to me. 'Goodbye, Doyley,' I said. 'For now.' 'What? Oh, are you off? Toodleoo then' he replied, and with that the whistle shrilled and the train pulled out, parting us in body, but never in spirit.

✳✳✳✳✳✳✳✳✳✳

As Sid has already pointed out, Trunch Central Station was some way from the centre of Trunch! In fact it was actually in the parish of St Just-near-Trunch.

Sid: When I was a boy I did a lot of train spotting at Trunch Central. Some days I did it for hours. Other days I got caught and had the paint confiscated before I'd got a single spot done.
   The station master was Mr Clerk. He could be a real stickler for the rules, could Mr Clerk. He once stopped Cecil Sharp, the folk-song collector, who was travelling from London with a first-class ticket and a bicycle. Mr Clerk reckoned he was a fare dodger, because he'd been travelling in the second-class. He made Mr Sharp pay the difference between the first-class fare and the second-class fare, which was minus fourpence halfpenny. Old Sharp was very decent about it by all accounts and tipped all the staff three halfpence each, so that was alright.
   It was a shame when they closed the station, 'cause there was something very romantic about it. And I'll tell you what it was – it was the space behind the bike sheds, underneath the arches. You could get in there for a bit of snogging and nobody would know. Nobody except the person you was snogging, that is.

25 January, Wednesday

Yesterday the snow began again and this time it has piled up in ridiculous amounts. Typically, nobody here seems to want to take responsibility for it or do anything about it. In London there were always people to sweep it from the roads, knock it off trees, remove it from the tradesmen, and so on. Here it is just left to lie, while the yokels stare at it in a witless manner. So I ventured forth to tea at the old schoolhouse with some trepidation. Huge banks of snow loomed above me in the dark as I made my way along the lane, and I wondered what rogues or vagabonds they might not conceal. I had my stout stick with me, as always, but the snow banks made it difficult to swing to full effect.

Miss Pickerel was most grateful to see me. The children, it seems, were excited by the snow and went wild in the playground. Her description of the smell of thirty damp children, steaming by the fire, quite revolted me and I was forced to change the subject.

28 January, Saturday

The snow, which the locals have resolutely failed to remove, is again beginning to clear itself of its own accord. The furrows of the lane are full of water, so I have not been out today. Nor has anybody called. This welcome respite from the hurly burly of social life has allowed me to reflect on my stay here and look forward to my departure in less than two months time.

Mr Fotherskill, who wrote today, said in his letter that 'St Just-near-Trunch has hardly changed since Domesday.' He seems to feel that this is a good thing. I have written to him, pointing out that the Normans gave this country a much needed shake up, having found it to be populated largely by disorganised, indolent peasants. I can only assume that they did not penetrate to this area, or perhaps decided that such disorganisation and indolence was beyond even their talents. They were, after all, only French.

The casual visitor, like Mr Fotherskill, might feel the village has a certain charm, but it is purely superficial. Beneath the crumpled chocolate box exterior lies a box of mouldy chocolates. Only the Great Hall stands apart, as a last bastion of decency and even there all is not well. Lord Silver-Darling is not the man he was. Some day, however, Doyley will come into his title and then, I think, with the right woman by his side, he might make something of this place.

 # FEBRUARY 1905

Rose's are red, Violet's are blue,
Mine are all pink, and this pair's for you.

(from a Valentine present in the Coote Memorial
Museum)

1 February, Wednesday

I called at the vicarage today, to ask after Rev. Mullett's chilblains. These he acquired while pursuing a fallen woman through the snow and for the past few days he has found walking most uncomfortable. On Monday I was so concerned that I had Maud make him some beef broth, to my own dear father's personal recipe. I asked how he had liked it. 'Well, dear lady, it has certainly cured my chilblains, but I don't know that the cure is not worse than the complaint.' I must have looked puzzled, as indeed I was, for he answered my unspoken question. 'You sent the most definite instructions that it should be thoroughly heated before use and as a consequence I have scalded both my feet.'

I was nonplussed, but did not pursue the matter as he was unable to spare me much time. It seems that the next two days are of great religious significance at St Just's and he will be kept very busy. He had asked Rev. Rudd to remove his slippers and socks, and he was writing his sermon for Friday. He declined to tell me his theme. 'All will be revealed in due course, dear lady,' he said. Unsure of quite what he meant by that I left quickly.

****

Once marking the end of the Christmas festivities, 1 February is Candlemas Eve. Clearly our ancestors had a lot more stamina than us! Candlemas itself marks the presentation of Christ in the temple and is celebrated with candles. In her book, *English Traditional Customs*, Christina Hole argues that this tradition goes back to the pagan Feast of Lights. In St Just-near-Trunch a candlelit procession was held until quite recently.

Sid: That was the war what put an end to it, because of the blackout. The ARP warden, 'Baldy' O'Hake, said they could only have a candlelit procession if they done it before lighting up time. Well the verger, who was in charge of it, weren't having none of that. 'That'd be a sunlit procession,' he say. 'Not if it was overcast' say the warden.

So the verger got up on his high horse, which was really a donkey, and set out to hold the candlelit procession anyhow. Now, I don't know if you've ever tried to hold a candlelit procession in a force 8 gale, but suffice it to say that 'Baldy' never even got a chance to say, 'Put that light out!' once, before it was put out anyhow. After that, everyone sort of lost interest and the next year 'Baldy' and the verger agreed to argue about something entirely different instead.

3 February, Friday

Yesterday we had special services and a candlelit procession. This consisted of vicar, choir and congregation traipsing through the village dripping wax everywhere and chanting. I cannot say that I approve of such theatrical goings on. They smack too much of the heathen. Today's service was more to my taste.

Today is the Feast of Saint Blaise, patron Saint of wool combers and diseases of the throat. At St Just's, Rev. Mullett has developed a reputation for its celebration, and wool combers and owners of diseased throats throng to the church from miles around. What a delightful service it was, marred only by the persistent coughing – caused perhaps by the little bits of wool which seemed to fill the air. It concluded with Rev. Rudd laying his hands on the throats of the sufferers.

Afterwards I congratulated Rev. Mullett on his sermon, which was based on the theme of wool combing. Much of the technical detail was beneath me, of course, but he delivered it with great gravity which, after all, is the important thing.

6 February, Monday

The weather today has been dull. Indeed, night began to overtake me as I returned from my daily constitutional. I quickened my pace, not wishing to walk these foreign byways in the dark. As I began the last leg of my route – the lonely lane which leads to the back of the Old Toll House – an eerie chanting came to my ears. I looked uneasily for its source and could have sworn that I saw a line of hooded figures moving through the trees, shuffling towards Trunch. I must admit that I completed the last hundred yards at a run, arriving home out of breath. Maud was somewhat taken aback by my appearance. 'There you go, ma'am. I told you all them walks would do you no good. Nobody round here walks unless they have to.'

I made clear to Maud what I thought of the habits of her compatriots. I did not tell her what had alarmed me, however, for it seemed somehow undignified.

Now I wonder whether I have not imagined the whole business. I am not superstitious, so I do not believe they were spectres. Perhaps they were real. But who in these uneducated parts would be able to sing in Latin? After a medicinal brandy I was ashamed of my weakness. I will set out tomorrow and investigate the phenomenon.

****

Maud's comment about walking remains true today. Generally speaking country people do not go for country walks – they prefer a day's shopping in town. It's city people who do most of the walking in the countryside.

The craze for these walks began in the 1930s, when bus loads of working people would come from the smoky towns on a Sunday, eager for fresh air and exercise. Many battles were fought over access, including the Trunch Trespass. This occurred because Lord Silver-Darling refused to allow 'foreigners' on to his land. He instructed his keepers to see them off.

One Sunday in August 1937, however, huge numbers of ramblers began to arrive outside The Goat Inn. The locals were concerned, fearing they might drink all the beer, but it soon became clear that they had other things on their mind. Alan Smith, who was one of the trespassers, recalls the event in his book *Marching To Gloria* :

As 2 o'clock approached a clerical figure began to address us from a soap box. 'We all know why we're here,' he declared. 'So let us go to it and may the Lord forgive us our trespass.' I wasn't clear which Lord he meant, but with his words ringing in our ears we set off, determined to gain access to the area known as Happy Valley. As we progressed we were surprised to find that our way had been made easy. Fences had been removed and signs hastily changed: 'Trespassers Will Be Persecuted' had become 'Trespassers Welcome'; 'No Entry, On Pain Of Pain' had become 'This Way, Please'. Puzzled, we pressed on till at last Happy Valley came into view.

And now we saw that the landlord had prepared a welcome for us after all. There were his keepers, each one well armed. One was armed with a large tea urn. Another hefted a tray of buns. Still another was festooned with corn plasters. Above them a sign said: 'Welcome to Trunch Leisure Park – It's Bootful'. And full of boots it was. Ramblers' boots, keepers' boots and all being urged to dance by the music of a huge steam organ.

To this day I am not sure whether we had a great victory or a great defeat. Or, indeed, a great draw. As we tramped home we were rather subdued. Somehow Happy Valley was not all we had imagined. Aside from the commercial aspect it was wet and boggy, full of biting insects and rather smelly. I never returned. (Chapter XIV – And Did That Foot?)

7 February, Tuesday

Today, armed with my stout stick, I set about investigating last night's apparition. I went to where I had seen the figures walking, which was in the woods at the edge of Away Farm. At once I saw that the green stuff had been trodden down and in the mud I came across the print of what looked like a sandal. Casting about I found a piece of rough, blue cloth which had been caught on a bush. Comforted by this evidence that what I had seen had undoubtedly been human, I was looking around for further signs when I had a terrible shock. A voice boomed out behind me: 'And just what do you think you're doing?'

I was so taken aback that I did not even point out that one should never start a sentence with a conjunction. I spun round, to find myself looking at Farmer Trout's knees. 'See this wall I'm standing on?' he continued, not waiting for an answer to his first question. 'This wall marks the edge of my land and you are inside it. That makes you a trespasser. No one has the right to walk here but me and my men. If you was to ask me has anyone but me and my men the right to go on that bit of land, I should soon tell you. No, they haven't, that's what I should say. So what have you got to say for yourself better than that?'

Usually his verbosity infuriates me, but on this occasion it worked to my advantage, allowing me to gather my thoughts. 'Indeed, Farmer Trout? Then perhaps your men normally go around in blue habits, chanting in Latin.' This clearly interested him. 'What do you mean?' he asked.

'Last night I saw a column of men walking along here, chanting, and today I have discovered clear evidence of their passage. If they may walk here, then so may I.' At this he seemed to forget what had gone before. 'You saw the monks?' he gasped. 'It's not fair. I've lived here all my life and I've never seen the monks.' With that he took off, shouting 'She's seen the monks, that's all,' and seemed to forget the previous matter altogether. Perhaps I should worry more about Farmer Trout's instability than any mysterious monks.

****

In fact there were monks in St Just-near-Trunch. There may still be monks there today. But they are very, very rarely seen.

The Justinians, known as the Blue Friars, are a unique and secretive order. There has only been one certain sighting of them since Mrs Prewd's, that being in 1964 when a Brother visited the Trunch Folk Festival to complain about the noise.

The order was founded by St Just, to carry on her good works after her death. For many years they were a nomadic order, keeping themselves to themselves, with no permanent home. A monastery was eventually built for them by Sir Hugo de Gimingham, in atonement for his ravishing a nunnery in a fit of youthful exuberance. In accordance with the wishes of the monks the location of the monastery was kept a secret and remains so to this day. Due to their extreme seclusion very little is known of them.

The only concrete evidence of their existence is the appearance, at irregular intervals, of quantities of the Trunch Punch, for which they are best known. This rather sickly beverage is made, according to the label, of 57 different herbs and weeds. Fifty-seven, it seems, is a number of symbolic significance to the monks. According to Sid Kipper the importance of the number is simple: 'It's exactly the number of weeks in a year – plus a few spare ones.'

Around Trunch it was considered extremely lucky to see the monks of St Just. They have been seen so rarely, however, that it's difficult to say whether or not there is anything in the belief.

8 February, Wednesday

At breakfast I told Maud about Farmer Trout's odd behaviour yesterday. For some reason I thought it might amuse her. Instead she ran at once to fetch a swineherd. She returned, not with the filthy yokel I had expected, but with the tall, ascetic old man who had read

177

at the vicar's Christmas event. He burst in full of excitement and explained that he was 'An Augustus Swineherd, the author.' Pulling out pencil and paper he proceeded to interview me about what he called 'the mystery monks'. I was so taken aback by his audacity that I answered his questions without question – as it were.

When he was satisfied that I knew no more I finally managed to turn the tables and ask him what his interest in the matter was. He revealed that his whole life has been dedicated to a study of the Monks of St Just, as he calls them. Every spare hour has been spent searching out their history, their liturgy and their works. He plans to write the definitive book about the Order.

By now he had heightened my interest, so I asked what he had found out about them. 'Well, aside from what you have been kind enough to tell me and despite drinking an awful lot of punch, I have found out very little. They are so very secretive. I do know that it is considered extremely lucky to see them. Why, oh why, have I never had such luck?'

As I saw him out my heart leapt to see Doyley Silver-Darling's carriage going towards the Great Hall. He is back in the village.

> Cleopatra virginae, tera incognita,
> In loco parentis Caesar, multi Kama Sutra;
> Awayday, awayday, loco in transit,
> Omnibus, St Pancreas, awayday.
>
> Troilus et Cresida, cum homo errectus,
> Strangulated hernia, coitus interruptus.
>
> Gina Lolabrigida, osteo arthrytus,
> In vino veritas, Peter Dominicus.
>
> Figaro in opera, minus a soprano,
> Allegro castrati, Dame Placido Domingo.
>
> Non compus mentis, continuo ad nauseum,
> Ad lib, etcetera, quad erat demonstrandum.
> (*Awayday*)

12 February, Sunday

I am very excited. I never thought to anticipate any of the common people's vulgar customs with anything but trepidation. Now I find the very thought of St Valentine's Day thrills me to my most private of parts. For now I see the chance to declare my undying love for Doyley and have every hope that he will do the same by me.

I was warning Maud not to receive any Valentine cards when she informed me that they are not sent here. It seems the local custom is to send the object of one's affections a certain item of apparel. I cannot in all decency name the garment, but according to Maud they are guaranteed to arouse the ardour of any red-blooded swain. My own blue-blooded Doyley, I thought, would surely be no less affected. I determined at once to declare my feelings according to local tradition. To this end I have been busy with needle and wool, as I understand it is customary to embroider an appropriate message or design on a suitable portion of the garment.

Since Maud inadvertently suggested the scheme she shall also help carry it out in like manner. It should be simple enough to outwit such a half-wit. Tomorrow I will send her to the Hall with my token in a parcel, telling her that it contains something quite different, a pair of gloves, perhaps. No – I shall not mention a pair as that is too suggestive of the truth. I shall tell her that it contains a single, very large glove, while all the time she will be carrying my message to Doyley.

I do so hope they will have the desired effect.

****

The custom of sending embroidered underwear to a swain is still common in St Just. Some people think it a rather crude way of expressing your feelings, but it can be done tastefully. Much of the embroidery is most delicate, with charming, innocent motifs such as a bird in a bush, a man in a boat or a cuckoo in a nest. Many interesting examples of this unique local art-form may be seen at the Coote Memorial Museum on any wash day. The underwear may be inspected more closely by appointment with the Assistant Curator, Miss Annie Kipper, though care should be taken in phrasing your request.

The puzzling thing is that I can find no record of the 'Giving of Bloomers' before the February of 1905, when Mrs Prewd heard about it from her maid. Since that date the idea has been very popular. The parish records show that Rev. Mullett received five pairs of undergarments in 1906, eleven in 1908 and a grand total of twenty-one, including a pair of long johns, in 1911.

The earliest example in the museum is thought to be from 1906 – the year after Mrs Prewd left. This sudden appearance of a custom, with no evidence of its prior existence, is very odd, and has taxed the minds of local experts.

Sid: Some people say Aunt Maudy just made the custom up to suit herself. They ought to be careful what they say, they did, saying a member of my family would do that. I make my living by telling people about old customs and things, and if it gets round that I make it all up I'll be out of work.

My theory about why it appeared then is this. I reckon people just didn't like to talk about such things before then. I mean, we are talking about things what are intimate, aren't we? I mean, if you get some knickers off a lady you don't go round telling everyone about it, do you? I know I wouldn't.

We may never know the truth of the matter, since Maud's lips have long been sealed, along with the rest of her, in the St Just churchyard.

13 February, Monday

I have completed my embroidery in good time for tomorrow. As the garments in question already bear my initials I have simply added Doyley's on the other side. I do hope he will like them.

While I have been secretly busy at my sewing Maud has been doing her own. She has not let me see the result, but I doubt it can be of much merit. Her undergarments are so scanty as to leave little in the way of a canvas. Still, I expect they are bound for some rough labourer, without the sensitivity to appreciate fine embroidery. Unlike my Doyley, who I gather is something of an expert on the subject. As I write Maud has just left, innocently carrying my carefully wrapped token. Under the other arm she had her own, which I have allowed her to deliver on the way back. I do hope she does not drop them.

I am so excited about the morrow. At last Doyley will know my true feelings. I only hope that he will be able to reveal his to me.

****

I've been lucky enough to get hold of Maud Kipper's underthings of 1905. Mind you, it's said in the village that I'm only the last in a long line. By today's standards they are far from scanty, and despite the ravages of time and what we must assume to be a moth, we can still appreciate the delicacy of her needlework. On the front is a large heart, pierced by an arrow, surrounded by the letters M and D. At the back there is a little poem, in the most delicate stitching:

> Here I sit, and when I do
> I always, always think of you:
> Whenever you come to my mind
> I seem to get a little behind.

Between the two is a letter X. I have been unable to find out the significance of this – perhaps it's simply for decoration. I asked Sid about it, but he just gave me a wink and said: 'X marks the spot.' I can't believe that. Surely if Maud had spots she wouldn't want to draw her Valentine's attention to the fact.

14 February, Tuesday

The blesséd day has arrived and with it at last a true declaration of love from dear Doyley. The darling has sent me a vest. Pinned to it is a card, though he has not signed it, and he has disguised his hand to look like that of a rough untutored lout. In my heart, however, there is no doubt. My love is requited. Excuse my trembling hand, but my fine stallion has not stopped at the sending of a vest; he has also made a tryst. I am to meet him this very evening behind The Goat Inn.

I admit I am a little surprised at his choice of rendezvous. It is not really suitable for the romance of two such as us. Perhaps dear Doyley has some sort of sentimental attachment to the rear of The Goat. I shall not question my love on this. I shall put myself in his fine, aristocratic hands.

As I went for my walk after luncheon I seemed to be floating on air. Everything seemed better and nicer than I could have believed. I was keenly aware of a fresh Spring breeze playing gently around me. I must remember to replace the garment I sent.

15 February, Wednesday

It was all a dreadful mistake! I had the most terrible experience last night and have taken to my bed in shock. It has all been too much for my delicate sensibilities. I did not meet Doyley. I cannot write more now.

****

Sid: Typical of a foreigner, that is. They get all excited about something and then, before you know it, it's tears before bathtime. That's why I do a bit of work for the Norfolk Anti-Tourist Board. I go round telling people how nice it is in Norfolk, and then I point out that it'll stay a lot nicer if they don't all go there and buy up our houses, and marry all our women. Old Prewd could have done with thinking about that.

16 February, Thursday

I am going to write the whole terrible story down here, in the hope that it will help me come to terms with the shock. I am a little calmer now, though I fear writing this will excite all those terrible feelings again.

I spent all of Tuesday afternoon preparing myself for my assignation with Doyley. Maud laced me tightly into my corsets, until I could not tell whether my shortness of breath was due to excitement or constriction. Then I donned but three layers of bodices and petticoats, before adding my prettiest crocheted blouse and a well-fitted skirt which flared out to a wide hem, giving glimpses of a full inch of ankle. Finally I splashed on the last of a very expensive eau-de-toilette which a friend had brought back from Paris. Then, bidding Maud not to wait up, I set out into the gathering gloom of evening to meet my destiny.

The nearer I got to the Inn, however, the greater became my apprehension. The dark lanes seemed to hold unseen menaces, even more fearsome than the visible ones they contain during the day. If only, I thought, I could have taken a chaperon, but of course I could not. I began to wonder why Doyley had not offered to call for me in his carriage. It is a careless lover who lets the object of his affections roam the countryside alone at night.

There was no going back, however, and I urged myself to recover my sense of adventure. Quickening my pace I began to hum one of Doyley's favourite tunes from Trial By Jury and before long I had almost regained my former jaunty spirit. Before much longer I had arrived at the Inn.

As usual the foul odour of beer filled the night air. Dim lights flickered at the Inn's windows and tuneless voices bellowed the words of some lewd song. As luck would have it there was nobody going to or from the Inn and I was able to make my way unobserved to the rear.

I do not know how long I waited there as the night deepened, shivering partly with cold and partly with anticipation. Eventually I became aware of a loud and startling sound from within a ramshackle outhouse that stood in one corner of the yard. It was the deep, resonant sound of air being emitted at high pressure from a small aperture, accompanied by awful grunts, groans and gasps which might almost have been human.

I was just recalling Uncle Wesley's adage that 'he who runs and runs away, lives to run another day', and wondering if it applied equally to women, when the door of the shed was thrown open. A figure emerged into the yard, seeming to fumble with the front of its trousers. Despite the darkness I knew it at once, by the parrot on it's shoulder. It was the ghastly Albert Kipper.

'Ahoy there!' he bellowed and I tried to fade into the shadows, assuming he was calling to one of his fellows from the Inn. His next words, however, left no doubt who he was addressing.

'Ahoy there, Miri me old darling,' he roared. 'Here we all are then! Me, you, and the night of a thousand and one stars. I knew you'd come when you got me note. "Albert," I said. "She's just playing hard to get. You're not dealing with some doxy from the docks. This one has got class, with a capital A." Well, what d'you say?'

'What d'you say?' echoed the parrot, leering at me with a lecherous eye, as if I had not already suffered enough insult.

I decided that the time had finally come to put that awful man in his place once and for all. I recalled Uncle Wesley's tale of the time he addressed one hundred cannibals on the subject of table manners. Drawing myself up to my full height I looked him straight in the eye and thanked him not to address his betters in such a familiar tone.

'I do not know what you are doing here,' I was saying, warming to the task, when he interrupted me.

'Doing here?' he laughed. 'Doing here! We both know what I be doing here – the same as what you be doing here, my little iceberg.'

'Iceberg,' echoed the parrot.

'What I be doing here is none of your business, you impertinent little man,' I snapped, forgetting the King's English in my rage. 'For your information I happen to be waiting for a gentleman, who will probably knock your block off your shoulders – and your parrot too – when he finds you accosting me in this disgraceful manner.'

'Waiting for a gentleman, eh? That's a good one, that is,' he cackled. 'I wouldn't say a gentleman exactly, me darling. Your fine gentleman has other fish to batter. But what I do say is that he who you be a-waiting for be here now before you. I be he and I be here, and now we can consume our partnership. Why else would you send me your knickers?'

'Knickers,' cried the parrot, as Kipper pulled from an inside pocket my oh-so-precious garment, waving them as if repeating his point in semaphore.

For a moment I was at a complete loss. Then the terrible truth crashed in on me. I recalled the rough, illiterate scrawl on the Valentine card; the peculiar stains on the vest; the odd choice of rendezvous. As I turned and ran home I realised bitterly what a fool I had been.

Writing all this has calmed me. It has acted like some sort of exorcism. I can see now that I have allowed myself to be ruled by my heart and it has led to this. From now on my head must be queen.

****

It's easy to see how Mrs Prewd was devastated by this incident, but let's not forget poor Albert. It seems that, despite his earlier doubts, he had eventually fallen head over heels in love with her. That's why Maud, seeing through Mrs Prewd's ruse with the parcels, delivered the gift to him. He tells us as much in his ghosted life story, *Ship Fashion and Bristol Shaped*:

A sailor, me hearties, is always at the mercy of the elements. At sea he is tossed from billow to barnacle by wind, tide and currents. On shore his heart is prey to the charms of doxies, damsels and dames alike. We sailors have a saying: 'You cannot choose your captain' and that's just as true for the captain of your heart. I mind once, during a spell ashore, when I fell for a widow woman who was well beyond my means. I courted her till she was blue in the face, but all to no avail. Then, just when I had given up any hope of a fair wind, she sent me something that let me know that land might be ho.

We sailors have a saying: 'A woman is like a woman.' Well, this one was. Fickle, she was, and left me broken hearted. I went back to sea with nothing to remember her by but the token she had sent me. But all's well that ends well. That token saved the lives of me and my three ship mates when we were cast adrift in an open boat with no oars and no sail. They took the wind as though made for it. And when we struck land on an island in the South Seas we was made Kings, all because of the strange device on our sail. (Chapter XIV – February Sails)

Poor Albert. Mrs Prewd doesn't seem to have considered his feelings any more than Maud considered hers.

18 February, Saturday

I have spent the past two days coming to terms with what has happened. Maud has said nothing, so I think I may assume her brother has told no one about the incident on Tuesday. It was thinking of Maud which started to turn my mood from one of misery to one of anger.

I began to wonder how my most intimate gift could have found its way into the horny hands of Albert Kipper. Then I remembered that it was Maud who had delivered it for me. I called her at once and demanded an explanation. She looked decidedly shifty, but there is nothing unusual in that. She swore that she had delivered my parcel to the Great Hall as instructed, left it with Doyley's man Herring and then returned straight home. Despite my close cross-examination with a copper warming pan I could not budge her. She even had the impertinence to produce a delivery note from Herring.

Is Herring, then, the villain of the piece? Did my gift ever reach its proper destination? The thought of my most intimate garments being passed from hand to hand around the village was

185

nearly enough to make me swoon again. I did not swoon, however.
I determined that I shall get to the bottom of this business instead.

****

Since his name has cropped up I shall let Herring tell us what he knew about
this episode:

> One year, on Valentine's eve, I was called to the door to receive
> a parcel for my Master. It was delivered by his village girl, Maud.
> I noticed she had another parcel with her, also addressed to Him,
> but when I asked her about it she declared that it had been wrongly
> addressed and said she would deliver it to its rightful recipient
> herself.
>
> On opening the package my Master grunted with delight and
> held up what looked like a small pair of ladies nether garments.
> There was some sort of poem embroidered on the back, which He
> read with obvious satisfaction. 'I must reply,' He said. 'Fetch one
> of my clean vests before I hit you.' I told Him there were none
> ironed, yesterday being washing day. He then demanded I bring
> one of my own and a laundry marker. He proceeded to write 'Wish
> you were here' on the front, and made me run after the girl and give
> it to her.
>
> Luckily she had not gone straight back to her employer's
> house, and I overtook her in the village. When I had recovered my
> breath I asked if I might be of service by delivering her other parcel,
> thinking I might learn something to my advantage. But she said
> that it had already reached its destination.
>
> So I learnt nothing, at the cost of a perfectly decent vest.
> (*What I Saw* : Chapter 4 – Under-foot Man)

19 February, Sunday

This morning I plucked up the courage to attend church. Despite my
fears I was not held up to ridicule. Rev. Mullett commented that he
had not seen me for a few days and asked if I were well, but
otherwise nothing was said.

Leaving church I grabbed Herring under the gargoyles. I put
it to him that he had been playing fast and loose with the affections
of others. He denied all knowledge at first, but as I made it clear that
his answers were not satisfactory he eventually told me a story about

Maud and two parcels. Then it all became clear. The stupid girl had simply muddled up the parcels. Which goes to show that while you may outwit a half-wit, the witless are beyond control. Why she had intended to give her own token to her brother I cannot imagine, except that it may have been a sisterly gesture to cheer him up in some way.

Once Herring had started to talk, however, he told me much more than I actually wished to hear. It seems I have been deluded in thinking that Doyley has some affection for me. He has, instead, been playing tricks on me for some purpose of his own. Herring, for instance, knew all about that business in October when Doyley cancelled our meeting. It seems he never intended to come at all. I cannot fathom his motives, but if that is his idea of a joke then I, for one, fail to find any humour in it.

What a fool I have been. While I have been feeling like a silly young girl I have actually been acting like one. So be it. Doyley will trifle with my affections no more, for I have wiped them out and replaced them with a cool contempt for one who so abuses his position. As Uncle Wesley would have said 'Handsome is as han-som cabs.' Let Doyley go to the devil. The matter is at an end.

I only worry how much Maud has guessed of the matter. Of course she is a simple, innocent child, ignorant of the finer feelings of life. I would hate to set her a poor example. She must save herself for a decent man, if there is such a thing.

✲✲✲✲✲✲✲✲✲

As I pointed out earlier it wasn't possible for Maud and Doyley to marry and she died a maid – in one sense of the word. She never bore children, but that in itself is perhaps not so terrible. I can't bear children either.

It's interesting that Herring was so forthcoming about the whole affair. Of course we know from his books that he had no great love for his master. He described him variously as 'a foppish fool', 'a pompous prig' and 'a stupid stuffshirt'. Perhaps he knew something about the incident of the polar bear and hoped for a repeat performance from Mrs Prewd. On the other hand he seems to have deliberately protected Maud from exposure.

Mrs Prewd took the news rather calmly and seems to have simply switched off her feelings for Doyley Silver-Darling, although some feelings returned on the eve of her departure.

23 February, Thursday

In a month's time I shall finally escape these odious parts and I have decided to hold a party to mark the event. I began today, by arranging for invitations to be printed. To this end I paid a visit to the printers in Trunch, which are run by a Mr Smith. I had the feeling that we have met somewhere before, but I cannot recall where.

'So, we meet again Mrs Prewd,' he said, after I had been ushered in by a girl. He had the advantage of me. As he showed me around his premises, however, something about his limp rang a bell in my memory.

He is inordinately proud of his business, which for some unfathomable reason is called The Garlic Press. 'We have all the very latest equipment,' he boasted. 'Here is our Phonocopier, which will take dictation and record it onto a wax cylinder. And this is our wax machine, which copies the cylinders and sends them by post anywhere in the county. As for typesetting, we have the most postmodern system available. All you need do is write your message on this piece of paper, here; press this button, here; and a postman appears immediately, there, to collect it and cycle over to North Walsham, where it is set the next day.'

There was much more of this sort of thing, but I had ceased listening. Eventually we returned to his office, where I told him my requirements. 'How many invitations will you be needing?' he asked. The question rather took me aback. How many people around here did I wish to invite? Just the few decent ones? Or the whole ragged populace, so I might gloat over seeing them for the last time? I temporised by instructing Mr Smith to have some samples prepared and sent to me. I arranged to let him know the numbers when, and if, I have approved his handiwork.

On arriving home I hit on a solution to the question of whom to invite. I will invite everyone, but require formal dress. This will automatically rule out the less desirable, as they will have no suitable clothing. I think it is a neat solution to a tricky problem.

****

Why was 'Skip' Smith so pleasant to Mrs Prewd? After all, his limp was her doing, following her visit to the bowls green in June. But, like many East

Anglians, 'Skip' was a patient man. This was his chance to get revenge, and he wasn't going to rush it. How he did it is still talked about in the village.

Sid: What old 'Skip' done was this: he made the samples just as she wanted, and got her approval and all that. Then he asked her if she didn't want the dee loo service. He said if she gave him the names and addresses of all the people, then he'd have them delivered for her. Well, she fell for it hook, line and plunger, and agreed. She even thanked him and give him a tip. So off she went home and off old Skip went to North Walsham, where he got them all changed. He only changed one little bit. He just changed 'formal dress' to 'fancy dress'.

25 February, Saturday

Today there was a wedding in the village and I must confess to feeling a little jealous. Not of the couple getting married, you understand. They are decent enough, I suppose, in so far as common people may be. He is a carter in the village and she is a school teacher from Knapton. I was jealous of the fact that from now on each of them will have a partner in life. When things go wrong they will always have someone to blame; when the whole world is against them they will have someone to take it out on. I miss my late husband in that respect. Uncle Wesley used to say: 'A woman without a fish is like a man without a bicycle' and I have often wondered what he meant by that.

I am not yet recovered enough from the events of that black day, February the fourteenth, to entertain the thought of matrimony for myself. I am a strong woman and being a widow gives me my place in the scheme of things. In fact, I have yet to reap the benefits of my status in any sort of decent society. In a bare month's time I shall be free to do just that and then I shall be able to forget all about my foolish infatuation for that man.

Such quiet contemplations on life were in stark contrast to the wild celebrations after the wedding. The formalities being over the party burst from the church, pausing only to have their portraits painted in the graveyard. Then the revels began. I crept home and barred the doors, but the sound of drinking and music could be

189

heard into the small hours of the night. And then on into the larger hours. I did not sleep at all well.

****

A wedding in the village was a big event. Lord Silver-Darling always gave the couple a pig and Cyril Cockle always gave them an old ginger beer bottle – though they always gave it back, which was why he was always able to give it to the next couple.

Oh when I was single I longed to be wed,
I thought I'd find joy in my wedding bed;
But I didn't find joy, I found Molly and Ned!
Oh I wish I was plural no more.

When first I got married I thought we'd spend hours
A-billing and cooing in love nests and bowers,
But now he just does bird impressions for hours,
Oh I wish I was plural no more.

Oh when I was single my mother would speak
Of rhubarb and oysters for men who are meek,
So I fed him that – he was sick for a week,
Oh I wish I was plural no more.

But although all we do is to argue and shout
Our union is strong, of that there's no doubt –
If we din't have each other what would we row about?
Oh I'm glad I'm not single no more.
(*I Wish I Was Plural No More*)

MARCH 1905

The Kipper Family Tree

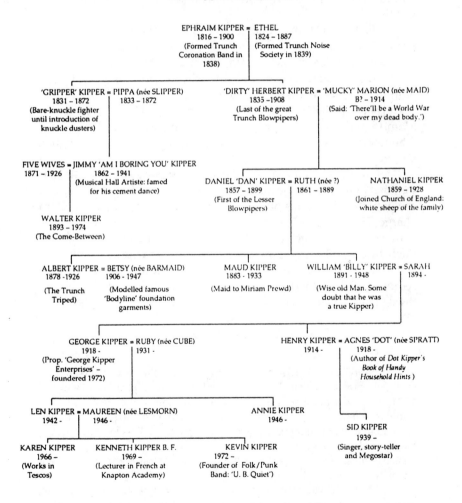

EPHRAIM KIPPER = ETHEL
1816 – 1900   1824 – 1887
(Formed Trunch   (Formed Trunch Noise
Coronation Band in   Society in 1839)
1838)

'GRIPPER' KIPPER = PIPPA (née SLIPPER)
1831 – 1872   1833 – 1872
(Bare-knuckle fighter
until introduction of
knuckle dusters)

'DIRTY' HERBERT KIPPER = 'MUCKY' MARION (née MAID)
1835 –1908   B? – 1914
(Last of the great   (Said: 'There'll be a World War
Trunch Blowpipers)   over my dead body.')

FIVE WIVES = JIMMY 'AM I BORING YOU' KIPPER
1871 – 1926   1862 – 1941
(Musical Hall Artiste: famed
for his cement dance)

DANIEL 'DAN' KIPPER = RUTH (née ?)
1857 – 1899   1861 – 1889
(First of the Lesser
Blowpipers)

NATHANIEL KIPPER
1859 – 1928
(Joined Church of England:
white sheep of the family)

WALTER KIPPER
1893 – 1974
(The Come-Between)

ALBERT KIPPER = BETSY (née BARMAID)
1878 -1926   1906 – 1947
(The Trunch   (Modelled famous
Triped)   'Bodyline' foundation
garments)

MAUD KIPPER
1883 - 1933
(Maid to Miriam Prewd)

WILLIAM 'BILLY' KIPPER = SARAH
1891 - 1948   1894 -
(Wise old Man. Some
doubt that he was
a true Kipper)

GEORGE KIPPER = RUBY (née CUBE)
1918 -   1931 -
(Prop. 'George Kipper
Enterprises' –
foundered 1972)

HENRY KIPPER = AGNES 'DOT' (née SPRATT)
1914 -   1918 -
(Author of Dot Kipper's
Book of Handy
Household Hints)

LEN KIPPER = MAUREEN (née LESMORN)
1942 -   1946 -

ANNIE KIPPER
1946 -

SID KIPPER
1939 -
(Singer, story-teller
and Megostar)

KAREN KIPPER
1966 –
(Works in
Tescos)

KENNETH KIPPER B. F.
1969 –
(Lecturer in French at
Knapton Academy)

KEVIN KIPPER
1972 –
(Founder of Folk / Punk
Band: 'U. B. Quiet')

191

1 March, Wednesday

Today begins my last month in this bucolic bedlam. It is Saint David's Day, but that is a matter for the Welsh.

Maud brought breakfast ten minutes late and I admonished her for it. 'I expect my breakfast to be ready when I wake,' I reminded her. 'Well you woke ten minutes early this morning,' she replied. I was not up to a proper reposte at such an hour, so asked after the weather.

'Just like a lamb, of course,' she said. At this I sat up and fixed her with a look which even Uncle Wesley would have considered old-fashioned. 'Of course,' I said. 'Of course, the weather is like a joint of meat. You will have to get up earlier of a morning to get away with talk like that. Take a month's notice.' She seemed not at all perturbed. 'It's just one of our sayings ma'am – March come in like a lamb and that go out like a lion.' Once again I was forced to wonder whether anyone here has ever had any regard for the English language.

Later I called on Miss Pickerel, to lay plans for my little get-together at the end of the month. Smith has completed the design of the invitations and has offered to have them delivered at no extra charge. How unexpected to find here the service – with that little extra servility – which one takes as a matter of course in London. Such uncharged items deserve to be encouraged with a generous tip.

Miss Pickerel and I are currently deciding on the victuals required and I suppose we must have something for the men to drink. I shall order an extra bottle of sherry from North Walsham.

✳✳✳✳✳✳✳✳✳✳

St Just-near-Trunch had, at one time, a group with the very highest regard for the English language. They were the leaders of the Pedants Revolt of 1781. This was another result of the introduction of the Pole Tax. The Pedants, led by What? Kipper – he always insisted on the question mark – claimed that the tax did not apply to rods or perches. If it did, they argued, then it would be called the Rod, Pole or Perch Tax. Using the opportunity to raise a number of other grievances they took to the streets with their popular cry of 'No taxation without punctuation.'

The revolt was short lived. As they marched through the village they began to argue, among themselves, whether they were marching up the main street or down it. This led to a split and the two groups decided to go their separate ways. As these ways were, in fact, the same way by two different names both groups stopped, drew their pens and began writing criticisms of each other. At this point Lord Silver-Darling arrived with a few armed men, and proved once and for all that the pen is no match for the sword.

7 March, Tuesday

Shrove Tuesday. For luncheon Maud served what she called 'panned cakes'. These were nasty, rubbery things, as unlike the crépes at the Ritz as Maud is unlike their chef, Monsieur Higginbottom. I ate them all; Lent is the season of suffering, after all.

This afternoon I went to the pharmacy to get something for my indigestion. Mr Carter gave me a green draught which tasted even worse than the panned cakes, but which helped immediately. I asked him about the ingredients. 'You'd rather not know,' he replied, with an impudent grin. I informed him that if I had rather not have known I would not have asked and insisted he detail the constituents at once.

After he had done so I left quickly, my stomach once again severely unsettled.

****

'Little' Carter's green draughts were much admired in the village. You only ever had to take one once and then the threat of a repeat dose would cure almost any complaint. 'You'd better take a green draught,' a mother would say to a child with a cough and the cough would instantly vanish! In fact the draught contained no active ingredients – just a mixture of all the nasty flavours which chemists keep to add to medicines. Plus one or two even nastier ones.

8 March, Wednesday

Thank goodness there is no local delicacy associated with Ash Wednesday. Today Maud just served up the usual burnt offering.

In the afternoon I took the train to North Walsham to shop. After St Just-near-Trunch this rather seedy market town can seem like a teeming metropolis. I placed an order with Mrs Braithwaite for a new gown for my leaving party and then walked around, window shopping. I am so out of touch. New fashions and inventions were in every shop, yet no doubt these goods are already out of date in London. I dare say it will take me a while to adjust. I will have to learn again what is what and who is who. One thing is certain, however: there will be no more eager student.

As a start to my studies I purchased a copy of last Friday's London *Times*. This only confirmed how out of date I am. For instance, it seems that during my absence Mr Winston Churchill has left the Conservatives and joined the Liberals, and we have signed a treaty with Tibet. Yet here it is as if these things had never happened.

I have arranged for *The Times* to be sent to me. Typically, however, they would not deliver daily. In London they will bring you the paper on the day of publication, but here I must accept a week's supply, delivered four days after the last issue. It will be worth it, however, to be sure that I do not say the wrong thing on my return. In London it is so easy to offend with a single wrong word. How unlike this soporific area, where it is often difficult to offend even when one intends to.

****

I'm not sure what Mrs Prewd meant by that last sentence. Why should it be more difficult to offend someone in St Just than in London?

Sid: It's all a matter of saying the wrong thing. And it's a lot worse now than it used to be. I mean, people get upset so easy nowadays. Years ago we used to spend a whole evening trying to get someone upset. You felt you'd achieved something when they finally lost their rag. Nowadays it's no fun at all, 'cause people get upset before you've hardly opened your mouth.

As a matter of fact you can have a lot of trouble with the folk songs, 'cause most of the things what upset people come in the folk songs. Things like hunting or whaling, or murdering people and cutting them up into little bits. Things like that. So what they've done now is to take some of the songs and take out the bits what might upset people and replace them with bits what won't. Then the songs become what they call Partially Correct. I don't think it'll catch on, though. I reckon those people enjoy getting upset.

> A young person was a-walking one morning in May;
> Met a second young person a-walking that way.
> Said the first of these people, 'I have Spanish leather,
> And oh 'tis my wish we were bonded together.'
>
> 'For the way I respond to the charms that thou hast
> I just cannot tell you, lest you feel harrassed.
> But you are so comely, and so fair of face,
> How I long to enter your personal space.'
>
> Said the other, 'I'm willing, if you would agree
> To place you above me and then underneath.'
> To a mossy green bank these two persons did haste,
> And there in a meaningful way interfaced.
>
> Both parties were eager, both parties were brisk,
> Both failed to ensure 'gainst a third-party risk.
> And so nine months later, as I understand,
> A third person singular came, all unplanned.
>
> Now the first person declared without guile;
> 'For your sweet sake I would lay down my life-style.'
> So these two were married, like sister and brother,
> And over the threshold they carried each other.
> (*All Things Are Quite Equal*)

12 March, Sunday

The first Sunday in Lent and the penultimate one of my self-imposed
sentence. My heart was light and I decided to take the long route
home from church, via the fields. Of course all routes in this
unkempt county go via some field or another, but this particular
way, to the back of the Great Hall, has more than most. I sent Maud
ahead to prepare lunch.

The fields soon spoiled my mood. They have become neglected again and it is such a pity. After the halvest last year they
were all turned over and tidied up, and left commendably flat and

195

brown. Unfortunately the indolent natives have since relaxed their vigilance and I noticed today that the green stuff is beginning to reappear. I must mention to Farmer Trout my scheme for killing it off now – nipping it in the bud, so to speak – rather than waiting until August as they did last year. It would save his men a great deal of work and leave them with more time for their animal impersonations.

The birds are back, also. I am no expert in such matters, but I believe this is the time of year when they build their nests. Would it not be more sensible for Lord Silver-Darling to shoot them all now, before they have multiplied?

It occurred to me as I entered the lane that with my efficiency, vigour and ability to reason clearly, it might even be possible to make this village habitable. Given sufficient time, that is. Of course, had things been different with a certain gentleman who is certainly no gentleman . . .

Uncle Wesley came to my aid, as he has so often. 'If beggars had horses the riders would wish,' he used to say. Somehow that comforted me enough to face Maud's cooking once more.

****

Sid Kipper was especially moved by this entry:

> Can you imagine what things would be like with someone like her in charge? What did she know about farming? I mean, she'd probably go and do something daft like have all the hedges pulled out for not being efficient – that'd beggar up the poaching good and proper. And then she'd like as not do away with grazing animals and things, so there'd be no muck for the rhubarb. I expect she'd stop all the rotating crops and have great huge fields just growing wheat and barley and bugger all else, so there'd be no decent vegetables worth nicking. We don't need any of that in Norfolk, thank you very much!

16 March, Thursday

I am slightly concerned about Maud. What will become of her after I leave? Having received a modicum of training and a taste for the finer things of life with me, how will she be satisfied with work on the land? She is certainly not suitable for much better; I would have got rid of her a hundred times if there were anyone else available. The best she can hope for is to sink back to the inconsequencial existence of the rest of her family, I suppose.

I tried to discuss the matter with her but she was most dismissive: 'My family have got by in these parts for as long as anyone can remember. Longer, I dare say. I shan't be starving.'

I showed her that I can be just as dismissive, and gave her ten days' notice. I shall not waste my concern on her again, however slight.

****

The Trunch area was full of Kippers, who would be sure to look after one of their own. As an exercise I've traced the Kipper family tree for them. I think you'll agree that it shows Mrs Prewd was quite wrong to call them inconsequencial. Their ancestors were probably more impressive than her's.

20 March, Monday

This evening I attended my last meeting of the Trunch Musical Appreciation Society. I wonder if they will be able to carry on without me? They are all coming to my little event next Thursday, so our final farewells will take place then.

Mr Babcock actually winked at me at one point and told me he was getting his costume ready. I said that a man in his position no doubt already had evening dress. Indeed he had, he replied, but he was having the devil's own job finding shoes and a handbag to match. Was this another of those joke things? There certainly seemed to be a misunderstanding, but I did not pursue it.

My mind was not really on the meeting. My mind is already in London. I have been imagining musical evenings of a much more sophisticated sort, in the company of a higher class. I had almost forgotten that I am only associating with these people because of the absence of anything better. Soon I will be able to look down on them almost as much as I currently look down on the rest of this provincial population.

With all this in mind I had Maud start the packing. The silly girl had no idea of how to begin and I had to watch her all the time.

I was quite exhausted by the time she had filled a dozen boxes or so, and sent her downstairs to fetch one of the big armchairs from the parlour for me to sit in. Clearly all my efforts to train her have been wasted or she would not need to be told. She has some notion of taking up a position at the Great Hall, but I fear she is quite inadequate.

****

The T. M. A. S. carried on for many years after Mrs Prewd's departure. It was still carrying on in 1972, when a friend of mine, Griff Codbold, moved into the area. He told me: 'It was just a bunch of ignoramuses sitting around discussing things they knew nothing about.' It's nice to know that some things don't change.

Maud Kipper, of course, continued to take up various positions at the Hall under Doyley Silver-Darling until his marriage in 1913. She had no trouble getting employment, either. After the war she worked as a barmaid in The Goat Inn, a waitress in Mrs Dace's Tea Rooms and for some years as housekeeper to Augustus Swineherd, as well as running her own business.

21 March, Tuesday

After a long day watching Maud carry trunks and boxes downstairs I went for tea at the schoolhouse. Miss Pickerel, I fear, will be lost without me. She insisted on telling me how wonderful I am, how much she admires me, how I have changed her life, and so on. Were it not true it would have been embarrassing. After much pleading on her part I agreed that she may write to me in London, though I made it clear that I shall not reply.

I think I may be proud of Miss Pickerel. She has come on a great deal under my influence. Her appearance, her manner and her self-confidence have all improved, although I have my doubts about her activities with Rev. Rudd. She says I once told her that every woman should have a hobby. Indeed I did, but I meant something suitable, like embroidery. Touring the area on the crossbar of a drunken curate is not, to my mind, quite the thing.

****

Miss Pickerel wrote a nice piece about Mrs Prewd's departure for the parish newsletter:

> Mrs Prewd was a woman who knew her place and was always ready to put others in their's. Her return to her belovèd London leaves us all the poorer. I feel sure that all decent people are sorry to see her go. She does so with our best wishes.

Mrs Prewd's leaving was a big event in St Just and is mentioned in a number of places:

> Parish Council Minutes: 27 March 1905.
> Any Other Business.
> Mr Clerk reported that the bossy woman who lived at the Old Toll House has gone back to London. He said that we were all a bit poorer for her leaving, due to the compulsory whip round organised by Lord Silver-Darling. He said no decent person was sorry to see her go and that she went with his worst wishes.

There were mixed feelings for Herring at the Great Hall:

> I recall an evening when my master was in especially good spirits. 'Tonight's the night, Herring you fool,' He said. I asked which particular night tonight might be. 'The last night of the Prunes, of course,' He replied. 'Tomorrow my little Fancy will be unemployed, but I'll show her how to put a loose end to good use, eh?'
> Thus began a period when I was often given the evening off while He entertained His village girl. I got to know Daphne, now Lady Silver-Darling's personal maid, in a most personal way, culminating in our marriage in the autumn of that year. I shall always hold Mrs Prewd to blame for that.
> (*What I Saw*: Chapter 9 – Human Bondage)

The young Augustus Swineherd wasn't old enough to realise the significance of the event, but he was clearly aware that something was going on:

> We children were very excited the night of the big party in the village. And we were very annoyed not to be invited. We all pushed our faces to the cottage windows and watched the grown ups go by. How jolly they seemed as they came laughing down the lane with their lanterns bobbing on the carts or carried on poles. What a night they must have had. I have often wondered what it was all in aid of.
> (*Saprise To Cringleford* : Chapter 8)

Finally, the Estate Diary of the time took a more practical line:

24.3.1905 — Old Toll House now empty.
Must find another city fool to take it on.

22 March, Wednesday

This afternoon my final preparations were interrupted by a visit from Farmer Trout. His visits in the past have often left me angry and frustrated, but today he did me a great service.

I was watching Maud carry the bedroom carpets down to the cellar for storage when his knock came. As she put down her load and answered it I took a seat in the parlour. On hearing his voice I called out that if he wished to enter he must first remove his muddy boots. This, however, proved to be a waste of breath, as he proceeded to stand in the middle of the room in extremely muddy socks. As usual he launched into his speech without invitation.

'Now see here Mrs Prude,' he began and I was delighted that he had finally got my name right – though something told me he still had the spelling wrong. 'It's about your do tomorrow. I'm very honoured to be invited, but I've never been so insulted in all my life. Of course I'd be delighted to come and I most certainly shan't be there. It was very kind of you to ask me and how dare you suggest such a thing?' I was wondering if there was any point in letting him babble much longer when he came to it.

'I have no intention of dressing up in silly clothes just to please you, thank you. It may be alright in London for respectable farmers to do such a thing, but here in the country it's not considered proper. Just because it suits you, you shouldn't assume that everyone else feels the same way, and I'm sure everyone else feels the same as I do. That's all I want to say to you, though I'd like to say a great deal more. But I shan't have a chance, shall I, it being a leaving party I'm not coming to. So I'll wish you well and good riddance.'

With that he made his usual abrupt exit. This time, however, I had nothing I wished to say to him. This time I was delighted he had called, for clearly my plan is going to work. Only those accustomed to formal dress will be attending my little event tomorrow. I do hope I have not ordered too much sherry.

****

200

If only Mrs Prewd had known the commotion that was going on throughout St Just. Her invitations – including their instruction to wear fancy dress – had been widely distributed by 'Skip' Smith, and in almost every house and cottage the women were busy with needle and thread, making costumes. A rumour had spread that a prize would be given for the fanciest fancy dress and that was a challenge no seamstress could resist. Old curtains, bed-spreads, potato sacks and even babies' bonnets were being pressed into service for the occasion. The variety of costumes produced was described in the report in *The Trunch Trumpet*, a week later:

FARWELL DO UNMARRED
BY SHOCKING INCIDENT

Last Thursday night a fancy-dress party was given by Mrs Prod, of the Old Toll House. Everybody was there, apart from Farmer Trout of Away Farm, who said 'I don't hold with fancy dress' – and a great deal more we cannot print here.

Everyone agreed that the fancy dress was very clever. Young Albert Kipper came as a three-legged milking stool and was so convincing that he persuaded Betsy Barbel, who came as a milk maid, to sit on him. Cyril Cockle came as a policeman and was arrested for impersonating an officer by Constable Crabb, who came as a burglar. There was some confusion when they arrived at North Walsham Police Station.

There was every sort of costume imaginable. Only the printer, 'Skip' Smith, let the side down, arriving in formal evening dress! The prize was won by the Lewis twins, who came as each other. When it turned out there was no actual prize they were awarded a bottle of sherry which nobody wanted.

The evening was marred only briefly by the violent incident which occurred. Nobody from Trunch was involved.

(*The Trunch Trumpet*: 31 March 1905)

23 March, Thursday

This morning all my luggage, but for a small suitcase, went to the station. I shall follow on the first train tomorrow. I am going to stay with an old school friend in London until I have received final payment for this diary and found suitable accommodation. The house seems uncomfortable again now it is empty, so I went for a walk this afternoon to take a final look at the village. I do believe there are one or two things I shall miss. My own pew in the church, for one. Miss Pickerel's adoration for another. I think that is all.

On my return I supervised the final preparations for this evening's event. Maud was especially argumentative, disputing my instructions at every turn. I plan to use just the parlour as I am expecting so few and this seemed to surprise her. 'You won't keep them all in here,' she said. 'They'll be all over the place. I thought that's why we cleared out the bedrooms so as things wouldn't get banged about.' I assured her that the people we could expect this evening would hardly be the type to bang things about in bedrooms. 'You know best, ma'am,' was her only reply. It is one I have come to fear, as it usually precedes some calamity.

No calamity has come yet, however. The sherry and glasses stand ready. The little dry biscuits which I got especially from North Walsham are next to them on the sideboard. Mr Babcock's record player, which he brought over yesterday, is ready to play something light but tasteful. Now I must pack this diary away for the last time, and go and prepare myself so that I shall be in plenty of time to receive my guests. Unless something exceptional happens this will be the last record of my stay in this putrid parish.

24 March, Friday – 1 a.m.

The exceptional has happened. The calamity has come. The first knock at the door came at 7.30, which was odd. The time printed on the invitations was 7.30, so I ought to have had at least another half an hour to dress. As I peered over the landing Maud came from the kitchen to answer the door, caught out in the same way, it seemed. For some unfathomable reason she was dressed as a butler, which I supposed was her misguided idea of suitable dress for a formal occasion. As yet, however, she had neglected to put on her trousers.

The oddness of Maud's appearance, however, was nothing to what was revealed at the door. It was like some dreadful nightmare. People began to flow into the house dressed in all sorts of outlandish garb. That first group alone included a nun, three school masters, and two and a half pantomime horses. They carried a variety of bottles, barrels and boxes. I immediately retreated to my room. Before long the sound of rustic music and raised voices drifted up from the hall, as more and more of them arrived. How could my plan have gone so wrong?

The evening was clearly ruined, but I decided that for once I would allow them to go to hell in their own pathetic way. Let them do what they would. I would lock myself in my bedroom until morning, when I would be rid of them forever.

Having decided this I felt better. Then I remembered that my suitcase, which contained my most precious possessions, was still on the landing. As I rushed to retrieve it another batch of guests arrived, including, to my absolute indignation, the ridiculous polar bear costume of Doyley Silver-Darling.

I was furious. How could he? In a few hours I would be gone, but he could not resist one last opportunity to humiliate me. I could see it all now. No doubt he had arranged the ruination of my little event. No doubt he had encouraged the others to don ridiculous costumes, and defile my premises with their drink and noise. No doubt he had induced Maud to remove her trousers. It was too much.

I was halfway down the stairs with the window pole in my hand before I realised I had changed my mind. I would not retreat to my room. I would take the attack to the leader of this rabble and put him to the rout. As Uncle Wesley was wont to say: 'Every worm has his turn.'

So once again I found myself giving that polar bear a thorough hiding. I delivered three or four good blows before I was dragged off by the Archbishop of Canterbury and Florence Nightingale, who turned out to be Rev. Mullett and Miss Pickerel. The bear had not even raised a paw to defend itself. As it fell to the ground its head rolled off, revealing not Doyley Silver-Darling but the bloody face of dear Percy Fotherskill.

For a moment I was nearly as stunned as he. Then, struggling free of my restraint I ran up the stairs, snatching my suitcase on the way and locked myself in the bedroom. It was all too much. I could not stay in that house a moment longer. I opened the window and, using the drainpipe to steady myself, climbed down on to the coalshed by way of the porch roof, and thence to the ground. I admit it: I fled. I had to be away from that place, which by now had every window ablaze and rang with the sounds of revelry. As I ran through the village in my bare feet it seemed deserted, without even a light at The New Goat Inn. Gradually my flight slowed, until I came to the station, where I took refuge in the waiting room.

Here I wait. In a few hours the train will take me away from this vile, ungrateful village forever. I shall not turn for a last look. I shall leave with as much dignity as an Englishwoman can muster.

My only regret is that I did not stop to put my gown on.

****

Mrs Prewd's 'little event' turned into one of the most memorable nights in St Just-near-Trunch for many years – what a pity she missed it.

Sid: She missed a good night alright. You see, they'd decided to give her a really good send-off and they weren't going to alter their plans just 'cause she'd already gone.

It was Miss Pickerel what sent for that Fotherskill bloke to come. She'd borrowed the bearskin for him and everything. He was carted off to Cromer hospital and then they had the telegrams. None had come for Mrs Prewd, so the postmistresses read out some others that came to hand – there was one from Wally Whiting to Widow Hake they still talk about.

After that the party really got going and it went on the whole night, right through to the morning when they had the mass procession. The idea was to process her from the Old Toll House to the station. There was the Plague Dancers in the lead, then everyone else, then the village band bringing up the rear. Of course, there was a gap in the middle where the guest of honour should have been, but they didn't let that spoil things.

In a way that was a good thing she'd gone ahead, because of what happened with Farmer Trout. He was still upset about the insult he thought he'd got, so he drove all his cows through the village ahead of the procession, to get his own back. No matter what anyone said he wouldn't shift, so the whole thing had to go as slow as his cows. Plus they was delayed by the dancers slipping over due to the cows doing their business. Add the fact that they stopped at The Goat Inn for a few on the way and they arrived at the station just in time to see the train disappearing down the line to North Walsham with her on it.

So that was the end of Mrs Prewd, as far as St Just-near-Trunch was concerned. She left without saying goodbye, but nobody seems to have minded.

THE END

Editor's Postscript

The reader may be wondering why this diary has come, only now, to be published, especially considering the dramatic way in which Mr Penguin's prediction about Edwardian ladies' diaries came true a few years ago. The fact is that Mrs Prewd's circumstances changed dramatically soon after its completion.

On her way to deliver the diary to Mr Penguin (who by now was no longer interested, having got out of publishing altogether and begun a very profitable line in chocolate biscuits) she met, and eventually married, her second husband. She paid back the advance and determined that no one should ever see the contents of her secret diary.

But for some reason she did not destroy it. Instead she placed it in the vaults of Cox's Bank, in Charing Cross, and never looked at it again. When it came into my hands it was still a secret. But, as the lady in question is long gone, I feel that the time has come for her diary to reveal its secrets at last. And since I find myself in similar financial straits to those she suffered herself, I feel sure she would understand.

Chris Sugden

Other Editor's Postscript

On the other hand the reader may not be wondering about why this diary was published at all; they may be wondering where they can hear more of my wonderful songs and stories, and wisdom that are in the book. The answer is that best of all they should come and see me at one of my jigs what I do all over the place if you keep your eyes open. Failing that they should get hold of one of my albums. There's one called *Like A Rhinestone Ploughboy*, by Sid Kipper, and it's on the Leader record label, number LER 2115, and it's distributed by CM Distribution.

Then on the other hand again, you may not be wondering any of this, in which case I'm sorry to have taken up your time.

Sid Kipper

So Martha this letter must serve to explain
That I'll soon be returning to London again.
My nights are all spent in the counting of sheep,
Then the birds wake me up just as I get to sleep.
The views are too roomy, the people ill-dressed,
And the air from the pig styes is simply too fresh;
I can't wait for the fog that comes rolling so grand,
Where the Charing Cross Road
Sweeps down to the Strand.
(*The Muntons of Moorgate*)

Bibliography

Dab, B. (Ed.): *The Boys' Book of Facts and Flags of All Nations,* 1957 (We Are Books).

Estate Diary for 1905 (Coote Memorial Museum).

Folk-song Society Journal, 1913.

Friend, A.: personal correspondence.

Grave, G.: *Golden Treasury of Music* (The Frank Press).

Herring: *I Did It* (The Trouser Press).

Herring: *What I Saw* (The Trouser Press).

Jane: *Jane's Fighting Drunks* (Jane)

Kipper, A.: *Ship Fashion and Bristol Shaped* (Unpublished manuscript in the Coote memorial Museum).

Manorial Records for 1672 (Coote Memorial Museum).

Marlin, V.: *Methodism in their Madness* (The Union of Sweedbashers and Allied Trades).

Mathews, Mrs.: *Pupils' Notes* (Knapton Museum of the Norfolk Language).

Nudds, D.: *Nudd's Nobs,* 1904 (Ffaber & Ffaber).

Perch, Dr G.: *The Insteps of St Just* (private pamphlet).

Shipham, Old M.: *Dream Report* (private papers of the Trout family).

Shock, F.: *Know the Game – Divining* (Old Poofs' Press).

Smith, A.: *Marching to Gloria* (Perseverance Press)

Smith, R.: *The Place of Underwear in the History of Dance* (EFSDS)

St Just-near-Trunch Parish Council Minutes, 1904/5

St Just Parish Newsletter (Coote Memorial Museum).

Swineherd, A.: *Saprise to Cringleford* (Swinebooks).

Swineherd, A.: *The Come-Between* (Herdbooks).

Trunch Trumpet: 31 March 1905.

Wilcox, W.: *A Straight Bat and other Improved Mammals* (The Imperial Press).

Wool Gatherer, The (1935).